EVERYTHING HAPPENED AROUND THE SWITCHBOARD

EVERYTHING HAPPENED AROUND THE SWITCHBOARD

by

Michael R. Hathaway

Library of Congress Catalog Card Number: 96-92972

Reflection Publications
P.O. Box 705
Conway, NH 03818

Printed by:
Cardinal Printing Company
Route 117, P.O. Box 115
Denmark, ME 04022

ISBN 0-9654159-1-0
Revised Edition

Front Cover:
Photograph by Bill Haynes
Sign by Mike & Penny Hathaway

DEDICATION

An eerie sound of silence descended over Barbara and Elden Hathaway's home the afternoon of October 11, 1983. I watched the room fill with people as the 2 p.m. cutover slowly approached. There was an air of sadness. I had been there at the beginning, and even though I was not involved in the daily operations of later years, I still felt close ties. Also present were the new owners, friends, family, neighbors, former employees, telephone history buffs, and members of the press.

The saga of the Bryant Pond Telephone Company had been closely followed throughout the nation. This afternoon would record its obituary.

My two sisters, Susan Glines and Linda Stowell, were tending the switchboards as the deadline approached. All the homes and offices in the calling area had new dial phones in place. The signal was given, and a stream of carbons were pulled from the old equipment and splattered on the floor.

It was over. The last magneto telephone company in North America fell silent and with it a way of life that had linked our country together for nearly a century.

This book is dedicated to the years of service my parents, my sisters, the operators and linemen gave to the community of Bryant Pond, Maine and to all those others throughout the country who helped enrich the quality of life through telephony. Finally, this book would never have come to fruition without the countless hours of work by my wife Penny Davis Hathaway.

Michael R. Hathaway

IN MEMORY

Elden R. Hathaway	1917 - 1993
Robert McKeen, Jr.	1925 - 1996

FOREWORD

We bought the telephone company in 1951 so that we could stay in Bryant Pond and raise our family. For 32 years the switchboards in our living room were the pulse of the community. Our lives revolved around them, and the operators were an extension of our family.

There were many independent telephone companies at the time, and it was unthinkable that we would stay in operation to be the last magneto system in North America. We had many struggles through the years, but loyal crew and staff were always there to give a helping hand.

We enjoyed serving the public and appreciated their concern when we were forced to sell. Mike has written this book to preserve the history and explain how it was done in the old days.

Barbara Hathaway

EVERYTHING HAPPENED AROUND THE SWITCHBOARD
by
Michael R. Hathaway

TABLE OF CONTENTS

INDEX OF PICTURES

Chapter 1 - THE BIG TIME
Photograph by Hathaway

"Elden's face...had deep weathered lines...down to his gray, bristly beard and up to his short 'crew cut' hair...Barbara fitted the description of a gentle matronly grandmother. She was just that..."

Chapter 1

THE BIG TIME

Labor Day, 1982...

The elderly couple was not used to flying. This trip, in fact, was only their second plane trip and the first one to the West Coast. Their busy and demanding life together had given them little opportunity for travel.

Elden's face reflected the rugged out-door life he had endured as a railroad man for nearly 40 years. It had deep weathered lines that ebbed and flowed down to his gray, bristly beard and up to his short "crew cut" hair. Despite his age, he was still a large and strong appearing man. The expanse of his stomach was a testament to his wife's ability to prepare delicious home-cooked meals.

Barbara fitted the description of a gentle matronly grandmother. She was just that, blessed with four grandchildren.

"These seats don't give us much room," Elden complained. "My hips and legs are killing me. I'll be glad to get my feet back on the ground again." Like his father before him, the constant pounding of riding the rails had taken its toll on his body.

"How do you think they are going to find us at the airport?" Barbara worried.

The plane began its final approach.

"Ladies and gentlemen, we will be arriving in Los Angeles in approximately fifteen minutes. Please secure your bags and prepare to fasten your seat belts." The Captain's voice sent a flurry of activity throughout the cabin.

The airport terminal was filled with holiday travelers.

"Well, at least we found our luggage," Barbara said with some relief as it appeared on the carousel. She had feared that they might not see it again.

It took some time for Elden to work the kinks out of his legs. "There's a chauffeur over there who seems to be looking for someone. Maybe he's waiting for us," Barbara hoped.

In fact the uniformed man held up a small sign with their last name. "I'll take your bags to the vehicle and pick you up right at the curb." He disappeared into the crowd.

"He looks more like a bodyguard!" Barbara whispered to Elden. She felt like pinching herself to see if all of this was a dream. "Imagine all this treatment!"

The limo arrived in front of where they were standing.

The driver jumped out. "Let me get the door for you," he politely commanded.

"I'm not used to this," Barbara replied. She was a little embarrassed over the special treatment they were receiving. The chauffeur helped them into the roomy backseat.

The traffic pace was fast and furious. "I'm glad I don't have to drive on these roads," Elden concluded. "This is worse than the summer Route 26 traffic going to Old Orchard Beach."

Their dream trip continued as they arrived at the Universal Sheraton Hotel. They were taken to their luxurious accommodations high up on the 17th floor where they could watch the hustle and bustle of Hollywood on the streets below. Helicopters shuttling travelers seemed to be at eye level with them.

After a short rest they ate in the hotel's cafe, enjoying not only the elegant food, but the jet-setters around them as well. Heads still spinning, they turned in early as tomorrow held promise of an exciting momentous day.

Even though they were tired from their journey, Barbara and Elden woke early the next morning. They explored the hotel and surrounding streets, passing the time until their luncheon meeting which was held at a Chinese restaurant a short walk away. They reminisced with their host over the last 30 years of their life. As the luncheon concluded, their host said, "Of course we want you both to go on the show."

"Oh no!" Barbara replied with terror in her voice. "I never make public appearances!"

"Well, you've been a part of it since the beginning, and I think you should take part in the program tonight," he insisted. The decision was made - they both would go on.

The afternoon seemed like a dizzying whirl. At 4 p.m. the limo returned to the hotel and whisked them off to Burbank.

"The Hathaways are here," he authoritatively announced as they arrived at the studio. The gates opened, and they drove through.

"Wow!" Barbara whispered. "Look at all the security!"

They were ushered to a comfortable dressing room. "Look!" Elden pointed out to his wife. "My name's on the door!" He was pleasantly surprised.

They didn't wait long. Next step was makeup. Elden's nose, broken many years before, needed extra powder to cut down the studio lights' reflection. Barbara thought they'd never finish fussing with her hair.

When the makeup artists were satisfied, they were taken to the "Green Room". That is the name generally given to the area where guests wait for their time to go on. Several other people were there sitting on comfortable sofas and watching a giant television screen. They were waiting for the show to begin.

"Oh, you're here," smiled the coordinator who had treated them to lunch earlier. "Is everything all right?"

"Do I have time for the bathroom?" Barbara asked.

"I'd like a little libation," Elden hinted.

"I'm in charge of both departments," the coordinator joked.

Barbara kept a tight grip on her pocketbook. It contained all the travel money they had brought from Maine, and it wasn't going to leave her side.

The show began.

"And here's Johnny!" Ed McMahon's familiar bar-room voice boomed throughout America.

Johnny's opening monologue brought several side splitting off-color comments - the kind that the host was renowned for. The curly-haired Deitrich of the Barney Miller Show, Steve Landesburg, was introduced to the audience. He and the host wandered through a spontaneous conversation that appeared to never get quite on track. Next Johnny brought on Cindy Morgan. She was doing publicity for her latest movie "Tron".

Family and friends back in New England waited nervously. It seemed that the show was moving at a crawl. Finally it was time for Barbara and Elden.

"And now, from Bryant Pond, Maine, we have Ma and Pa Bell, Barbara and Elden Hathaway!" Into the glare of the television lights they stepped. They were there to tell Johnny all about the old-fashioned hand crank telephone company they had owned for the past 30 years. It was now the last one in operation in the entire country.

Elden did most of the talking. He was used to doing interviews. Barbara sat silently and smiled as Johnny gently probed with questions designed to bring humorous responses. Finally, he turned to Barbara and asked, "What did take place around the switchboard?"

"Why EVERYTHING happens around the switchboard!" she replied. Johnny raised his eyebrows and gave that devilish look of his. The audience whooped with laughter.

For Barbara and Elden Hathaway of Bryant Pond, Maine, over the past three decades, almost everything in their lives HAD happened around the switchboard.

Chapter 2

JUST WHEN THINGS WERE LOOKING UP

Spring, 1951. Bryant Pond, Maine.

The year was going to be a good one for Barbara and Elden. Finally, after fifteen years of seasonal work for the Canadian National Railroad, Elden was in line for a full-time job. He had started working there in 1936, right out of high school. His hopes were to follow in his father's footsteps, climbing the ladder of security. He had begun working on the "extra" gangs that spent the summers upgrading track and building new spurs, tracks that helped connect businesses to the main line. It was a hot tiring job which required lifting the rails and ties into place, driving spikes, and shoveling dirt. Many of the laborers were French Canadians who spoke little English.

At that time the railroad was a major form of transportation for both freight and passengers, connecting the towns along its line from Portland, Maine to Island Pond, Vermont and on into Canada. Barbara and Elden had never owned a car. They walked or rode their bicycles the mile and a half to the train station every time they wanted to travel outside the community. The railroad gave passes to their employees' families allowing them to ride free up and down the line.

Summer evenings saw Elden, his father Rupert, and many of the town's men involved with their favorite pastime, baseball. At Town Meeting the citizens had even voted to build a ballfield rather than a municipal water system.

Bryant Pond, part of the township of Woodstock, is located in western Maine in the foothills of the White Mountains. It had a population in 1950 of less than 1000 residents. The village proper lies at the foot of "Merryfield Hill" and spreads out toward 3-mile long Lake Christopher, so named for Christopher Bryant, the town's founding father. Bryant Pond has been an attractive area for summer tourists since before the Depression.

In the '50s, most of the residents were employed at one of the two woodworking mills that produced clothespins and turned wooden handles. The Maine winters were hard, and with the "extra gang" laid off, Elden would usually find work at one of these mills or the canning factory in nearby West Paris.

He and Barbara were married in 1938. They met while taking part in a local community stage production. She came from Locke Mills, the next town up the railroad line. They built a home on Rumford Avenue in 1940 from lumber harvested from the debris of a hurricane that had devastated part of the area two years before. Leslie Davis and his crew from Bethel cut and sawed the timber and put up the house for $1200.

Their first son Michael was born in 1942, and in 1943 Elden was drafted into the Army. Susan was born in 1944. The young family struggled to survive the post war years existing on their seasonal jobs. Barbara baked goods and sold them through the local grocery store. Her bread, rolls and donuts, family recipes handed down through the years, were well liked by her customers.

By 1951 Elden's seniority on the railroad and the potential of a year round job gave them an opportunity to feel that things were finally looking up. They looked forward to a happy, active and secure life for themselves and their children.

- - - - - - - - - -

"The railroad is lengthening the section crew's responsibility from 7 to12 miles,effective immediately." The notice stunned Elden and the rest of the track crew. This meant he no longer had a chance for a full-time job. He felt as if all the years of patient waiting were for nothing.

"I wish there was something else I could do right here in town," Elden said to his wife as they pondered the devastating news. "If I stay with the railroad, we'll have to move." The couple talked for a long time about their options. Their roots were in Bryant Pond. They did not want to leave.

- - - - - - - - - -

At that moment the phone rang. Sylvia Judkins was calling to chat with Barbara. The Judkins lived at the beginning of the avenue and, despite a considerable difference in age, were good friends of the Hathaways. Both couples were active in the Eastern Star. Howard Judkins and his wife had moved to Bryant Pond a few years earlier and purchased the local telephone company known then as the "Bryant Pond Telephone Lines".

"Ask her if she wants to sell the phone company," Elden joked to his wife.

“Yes!” came the response. It was so loud that Elden heard it clear across the room.

"Tell her we'll be right down!" he shouted back.

Chapter 3

SO YOU WANT TO OWN A PHONE COMPANY

By 1951 Howard and Sylvia Judkins were ready to retire. He was a tall slender gravelly-voiced man and a staunch Republican who looked a little like Dwight D. Eisenhower. Sylvia's pleasant "Number Please" had established her as part of each customer's family. The phone company was located in their home at the beginning of Rumford Avenue near the base of Merryfield Hill. The switchboard was conveniently placed between the kitchen and bedroom where it could be tended easily both night and day. The apartment upstairs was rented to the McKeen family. Bob, Jr. had only to come downstairs to tend the board when it was time for his shift.

"So, you want to own a phone company," Howard said to Barbara and Elden as they sat down to a cup of coffee at the Judkins' kitchen table the same evening.

"Yes, we are definitely interested, if we can afford it," Elden replied. "I don't have much money in my pocket, but I'd be glad to give you what I've got for a binder until we decide."

"That won't be necessary," Howard responded. "We're ready to retire, and your word is good enough. If you don't want to purchase it, then that's all right too."

"How much do you think you want for it?" Elden asked, holding his breath.

"We'd like to get $2500." he replied. "Sylvia and I will finance it. You can pay us $19.15 a month for 15 years. All the phones and some of the lines are owned by New England Telephone Company. You'll have to rent them as well as lease pole space from the power company."

"That sounds like a fair price," Elden quickly responded, breathing a little easier. "If we're going to own the company, we will have to have Bob McKeen work for us. If he says OK, then we'll buy the business," he told the Judkins.

Bob was tending switchboard while the two couples were talking. They didn't waste any time. "If we buy the phone company," Elden asked, "will you continue to work on the switchboard for us?"

The proposal took Bob by surprise. He thought a moment and responded, "Well, yes, I'd be happy to."

Barbara and Elden had no knowledge of what it was like to run a telephone company. Not only was it necessary to be able to tend the switchboard, but they also would have to repair the lines and install new phones. They knew they could not manage alone. Bob McKeen was the key to their being able to stay in Bryant Pond.

With Bob's affirmative answer and the generous terms offered by the Judkins, Barbara and Elden said, "Yes, we'd like to buy the phone company."

- - - - - - - - - -

"What do we do next?" asked Elden after the initial shock had worn off.

"Well, first you have to get permission from the Maine Public Utilities Commission - they control all the phone companies in the state. We need to make an appointment with them."

The appointment was made, and Elden and Howard traveled to Augusta to meet with the Commission.

"Do you feel Mr. Hathaway is capable of running the telephone company?" they asked Howard.

"Yes, he is," was the reply.

"Then we approve the sale."

It had taken less than an hour. Now that permission had been given to purchase the company, there were still a few unsolved problems.

- - - - - - - - - -

"Where will we put the switchboard?" Barbara asked.

"Well, we don't have room for it and the family too," Elden responded.

After a lot of brainstorming, they decided to build a room onto the back of the house. However, this created one interesting dilemma. The bathroom window would now open into the telephone office.

Barbara's father Jason Bennett was in charge of the building project. He was an accomplished carpenter, and although partly disabled from a heart condition was happy to offer his assistance. The 10' x 24' telephone office on the back of the house was completed by the end of the summer. It overlooked a bog teaming with wildlife, birds, ducks, frogs, blue heron, and an occasional moose.

The Hathaway home was located just about a half mile up Rumford Avenue from the Judkins. Elden continued to work for the railroad by day, and he spent his nights and weekends stringing telephone wire between the Judkins' and the new office.

Getting ready to move the switchboard was a formidable job. Elden needed a lot of help.

Army surplus wire came rolled around iron reels. When the reel was laid on its side over a spindle with an iron rod in the middle, the line could be pulled the half-mile between locations. This was a good task for Mike, the Hathaways' nine year old son, but it was not as easy as it sounded. There were many trees on the street, and the line had to be threaded through them.

Elden found a solution for this problem by putting a screweye into a baseball. With a little slack in the wire, the ball could be tossed over the limbs so that Mike's journey up the street could continue. By the time he got to his house, the pulling resistance was great enough to leave red marks on his hands even though he was wearing gloves.

A neighborhood pal of Mike's, named Charlie McAllister, was a great help also. He even found a pair of lost pliers after Elden had lost them in a pile of leaves.

Elden spent hours climbing poles and securing the telephone wire. He numbered each line carefully on both ends. This made it easier to identify and connect after the switchboard was moved.

"Let me give you a little advice about climbing poles," Howard advised Elden after watching some of his early attempts. "Always wear a pair of suspenders! When I first started, I went up a pole to fix a wire and hooked my safety belt to hold me in place while I was doing the repairs. When I was done, I sucked in my breath and leaned closer to the pole so I could unhook the belt. The darned thing slipped all the way to my ankles. Worse yet, it pulled my pants down with it! There I was - up the pole in my underwear, and I couldn't reach down to pull up my trousers 'cause I'd fall. The only thing I could do was inch my way down to the ground. From that day on, I've never climbed a pole unless I was wearing suspenders!"

There were three very important pieces of equipment used in climbing telephone poles. First, the hooks, called "spurs", were a metal brace that went under the instep of a boot and extended a short way up the outside of the foot and up the leg on the inside about two-thirds of the way to the knee. Straps at the top and outside bottom held the spurs in place. A sharp steel point was welded to the brace just above the instep. This point was jabbed into the telephone pole each time the lineman climbed up or down.

A second item needed for climbing was the lineman's gloves. They had 3 to 4 inch cuffs which helped keep splinters out of the worker's wrists and arms. It was also advisable to wear a long sleeved shirt.

The third piece of equipment was the lineman's belt. It was made of thick leather a couple of inches wide and fastened around the waist by a large buckle. The side and back of the belt had various loops and pouches to hold the tools needed for pole work. A leather safety strap with metal snaps on both ends hung from a metal loop in the tool belt half way around the lineman's side. Once he was in place up the pole, he would unhook one side of the safety strap, place it around the pole, and hook it to another loop on the other side of the belt. Next he would gently ease backwards, testing the safety strap, and when satisfied that it was holding, he would be free to use his hands for line work. The lineman was only connected to the pole by the points of his spurs and the safety strap.

Chapter 4 - FROM NEIGHBORHOOD LINES
Photograph by Bill Haynes

"Bob McKeen continued to work for the telephone company after the sale." He is pictured here in 1979.

Chapter 4

FROM NEIGHBORHOOD LINES

Telephones first came to Bryant Pond in the early 1890's. They started out as a way to communicate with houses within one neighborhood. As many as a dozen families would get together and purchase the phone equipment from a mail order house such as the Chicago Telephone Supply Company. They would work together putting up the wire, usually by running it along fence posts or hanging it on trees. They only used poles cut from cedar trees when there was nothing to hang the wire to, or when crossing a road. The quality of reception was scratchy. Often the line would break, caused by fallen tree limbs or winter ice storms. However, when everything was working, regular Sunday afternoon gatherings were held by telephone. Sometimes a talented family would provide a musical concert for all the listeners.

These neighborhood lines began to link the community together. As telephones became popular, more neighborhoods followed suit, constructing their own lines. Soon a desire and need grew to find a way to link these individual groups together. This was accomplished by installing a switch in the home where one line stopped and another began. The switch allowed two neighborhoods to be joined together.

By the early 1900's much of Bryant Pond was covered by a network of neighborhood lines. A switching fee of two cents was charged for each inter-neighborhood call, and each group of owners had their own "officer-in-charge of keeping the connections running smoothly".

By 1907 the number of inter-neighborhood calls had increased so much that the switching process was no longer effective. It was decided to install a central switchboard in the village of Bryant Pond. All these individual phone systems were then connected in one place, and during the time when the operator was on duty, an individual at one end of town could talk to someone on the other end of town without going through several different switches. The following year the towns of Bryant Pond and Locke Mills were brought together by a phone line.

Live communication with the outside world had begun.

The Village Phone Company was run for a time by a local character named Doc Heath. He proved to be better at trading horses than he was at running the phone company. It didn't take long for him to send the business into bankruptcy. Other attempts to keep the operation solvent failed. The citizens of Bryant Pond once more found themselves without a central switching system.

At the end of the 1920's Carl Dudley and his wife installed a switchboard in their grocery store and operated it during the hours they were open for business. They had been convinced by New England Telephone Company to install a pay phone at that location a few years earlier.

The Dudleys owned the company until 1939 when they sold the business and the switchboard to Herbert and Viola Meserve. The Meserves purchased a small switchboard to keep in their den next to their bedroom. They were able to provide night phone service. In the fall of 1946 they hired a young Army veteran Robert McKeen, Jr., to work for them as a telephone operator.

That same fall, the Meserves sold the company to Howard and Sylvia Judkins. The Judkins moved the switchboard to their home on Rumford Avenue. Bob McKeen continued to work for the telephone company after the sale.

At the end of the Second World War a large amount of surplus telephone wire could be purchased at low prices. The military had needed wire that could be rapidly rolled out over the ground, allowing phone communication with the front battle lines.

The Army field wire consisted of two strands of wire covered with a cotton fiber casing. Each strand was actually made up of seven very small wires. Some were steel for strength, and the others were copper for quality of transmission. The surplus wire was easy to pull off the reel it came on and was easy to hang on the poles. It could be hung by clips, and in the case of many wires together, by a leather saddle.

Earlier telephone lines had been iron wire with no covering. Each separate line required two such wires. They were attached to glass insulators that had been screwed onto brackets hammered into a pole. In case of many lines, crossarms were attached to the poles. The open wires still crossed easily, causing a ground and an outage of phone service.

Chapter 5

THE CHANGE-OVER

The town of Bryant Pond kept close watch on the activity taking place on Rumford Avenue as Elden and his crew continued to work. The canvas saddles holding the wires on the poles looked like they could hold no more.

"I understand you bought the telephone company. Who's going to help you move it to your house?" inquired Clarence Todd one night at a Masonic meeting. He was the manager of the West Paris Telephone Company.

"I don't know. We haven't gotten that far yet," Elden replied.

"Let me know if you need help, and I'll come up and move it for you if you want."

"You've got the job!" Elden responded with an immense sense of relief.

By the end of November, everything was ready. All the lines were up, and the new room was finished. Barbara spent a lot of time at the Judkins learning how to run the switchboard. She knew it would be necessary for her to put in long hours once the move was made.

The day finally arrived. Clarence Todd brought up his truck.

Bob McKeen called all the customers and told them, "The Company will be out of service for four or five hours while it changes stations to the Hathaways' house."

Clarence took charge of the operation. "First we'll cut the wires at the Judkins, then move the switchboard, and solder the lines back on at Barbara and Elden's," he explained to the crew.

The switchboard was about six feet tall and somewhat resembled a high old-fashioned desk. The telephone operator had to sit on a stool in order to tend it. The working area was a flat surface lined with a double row of cords and plugs. There was also a row of black handles called keys. The operator could open a line and talk to a customer by pushing a key forward. To ring a caller, the key was pulled backward. The operator varied the length of the ring by the length of time the switch was pulled. The upright portion of the switchboard was full of empty holes, each with a hinged and numbered cover called a "drop". The backside of the switchboard was a maze of wiring connecting the front drops to the outside lines.

A caller would generate an electrical current by turning the crank on their phone. The current would travel through the wire and knock down the drop on the switchboard. The operator would then put a plug into the hole beneath the drop and answer "Operator". The caller would tell the operator who they wanted to call. The operator would then connect their plug into the correct drop and ring the number. The switchboard's ringing power came from dry cell batteries, or in case of emergencies, a generator crank.

In order to talk with a customer, the operator pushed the ringer key forward. In order to listen without being heard, a monitor button was pushed while the key was in the forward position. The monitor was basically used to tell if a caller had reached its party or finished its conversation. There was an ordinary clock over the switchboard to time any toll calls.

The lines were numbered numerically from one upwards, and the rings were either long or short. A "party line" which had more than one customer would have different special rings for each. For example, line four might have four customers. Their calling numbers might be "four ring three" (4-3), three rings of equal length, or "four ring twelve" (4-12). This number had one long ring followed by two short ones. Private lines had only one subscriber and needed to have only one ring, unless different members of the family wanted different rings.

When Barbara and Elden purchased the company, there were 37 lines and 100 subscribers. There were also two privately owned "farmers' lines" with 18 subscribers. They were the last of the old self-owned and maintained neighborhood systems dating back to the turn of the century. The two lines were in very poor shape and very hard to use. Shortly after the purchase, the owners asked the Hathaways to take over and upgrade them.

- - - - - - - - - -

The moving went well. By 11 o'clock at night everything was hooked back up, and Clarence said goodnight.

"I guess I'll call Mother," Elden said after Clarence left.

So he tried his first call. "That's funny...I know Mother's home, and I can't reach her."

Panic began to grip Elden. Barbara and he were now alone, and the board wasn't working! About that time they both wondered if the new venture was such a good idea.

Slowly and methodically, he began to look at all the wires. "I really don't know a thing about what I'm doing," he admitted.

Barbara looked worried. "Even if Clarence was home, we couldn't call him," she said.

"All the connections in the back look OK, and wiggling things isn't helping," Elden replied.

Anxious moments went by.

"Wait a minute! Here's a loose wire near the batteries. Let me see if I can find a place for it." The batteries were unhooked, and without power it was impossible to call out from the switchboard without using the auxiliary crank.

"Try ringing now," he told Barbara.

"Hello," the comforting sound of Mother Hathaway came over the line.

"Am I glad to hear your voice!" Elden said. "I guess I just fixed my first telephone trouble."

"Well, let's put the night alarm on and go to bed. I'm exhausted!" Barbara said. "I hope we don't sleep through any calls."

The couple spent a restless night in their bedroom next to the far end of the telephone office. It was as bad as having a newborn baby in the house.

"Gee, we really did it," Mike said in the morning as he came downstairs and eyed the switchboard. His father had already left for work on the railroad.

"You'll have to get your own breakfast. Bob isn't here yet, and I'm busy answering calls," his mother told him between conversations with the customers.

By now Susan was awake and had nestled up to Mother at the switchboard hoping to hear what the caller was saying.

The two children's minds were not on their schoolwork that day. They hurried home to see how things were going. The long wait had finally ended. The telephone company was now part of their family.

Chapter 6

THE EQUIPMENT

When Barbara and Elden purchased the telephone company, they got the rights to give service to the Bryant Pond area, the repair equipment and a 16 foot ladder. Most of the customers were on a party line and were billed $1.75 a month for phone rental with $.25 off if paid within ten days. The rates for private lines ran $2.24 for a residence and $3.00 for a business. Any toll calls made during the month were added to the bill.

"What are you going to do with the old car," inquired Elden of Howard. He was referring to the 1934 Plymouth Coupe, complete with rumble seat that was used to drive to line repairs. It had never started well and fortunately had a hand crank for when the battery ran down.

"Well, I don't really need it, and I guess if you'll give me fifty dollars, it's yours," Howard replied.

Elden bought it, but it spent a good part of its life at Harold Tyler's Garage where he tried to keep it in running condition.

Besides hiring Bob McKeen, Elden and Barbara were able to convince Howard's lineman Fred Farnum to continue working part-time. He knew how to fix the things that Elden was still learning how to do. The old Dodge was NOT Fred's favorite project. He often complained to Elden,

"This car has got to go. My arm is falling off from cranking it," Fred complained. "You can't fix a telephone without a way to get to it."

"Well, I was afraid that was going to come sooner or later," Elden agreed.

The Hathaways located an old 1942 Oakhurst milk truck for sale and scraped up enough money to buy it. Elden painted it a coat of dark green, and it was ready to go. There was only one problem. Elden didn't have a driver's license - never needed one while he was working on the railroad. Whenever Fred wasn't available, Barbara had to drive her husband to fix the phone troubles.

At the same time they were trading vehicles, the Hathaways got some more disturbing news. "This notice is to inform you we will no longer lease telephone equipment as of January 15, 1952." The letter from the New England Telephone Company hit hard. After only a month of ownership, they were going to be forced into further debt.

Elden called Clarence Todd for advice. "What do you think?" Elden. "We're sending them $30 a month now, and I wonder how much more they'll want?"

"I wouldn't worry too much," he replied. "New England has always been fair to us, and I'm sure they will be with you."

Elden and Barbara held their breath and waited. It wasn't until July when a N.E.T.C. representative called on the Hathaways.

"Well, I guess you probably know what I'm here for."

"I'm afraid we do, and I don't know how we'll be able to pay for the equipment," Elden replied. "We're just about breaking even as it is now."

"You've been paying us a lease every month, haven't you?" he replied. "All you've got to do is continue to pay the same amount, only instead of renting, you'll now be buying the equipment. Here is an inventory. You can look it over, and if it is somewhere near right, you can sign this-here bill-of-sale, and when you've paid enough, the equipment is yours."

"What a relief," Elden said, feeling a weight lift off his shoulders. "Clarence was right. You are fair."

Within the next year, they owned all the phone equipment.

Chapter 7

LIFE AROUND THE BOARD

From the day the switchboard moved to the Hathaways', their family life-style changed drastically. Almost everything in the house centered around the phone company.

Bob McKeen soon found that it would be a lot different working at the Hathaways'. They had two active children.

"Can you kids keep it a little quieter!" Bob would often have to ask as Susan and Mike squabbled over who would get to sit next to the board.

Meal schedules had to be adjusted. A good many of them were moved from the dining room table to portable trays in the office. On holidays the entire celebration was planned around the switchboard, allowing either Barbara or Elden to eat and answer calls at the same time. The family's merriment had to be tempered to fit the number of calls coming in. A "shhh!" from the operator would be a signal for more silence.

Bob worked mornings from 8 a.m. to 12 noon. In the afternoon Barbara would dash out to the kitchen between calls to start a roast or put the potatoes on. The ironing board was set up near the switchboard, and all the mending was done there as well. Bob's second shift started at five p.m., which did allow an evening family meal, providing there weren't any line troubles. Many times Elden had to eat warmed up leftovers after he returned home from telephone repairs. He would often be so tired he could hardly taste the food.

Mike's keen nose kept his mother apprised of the meal progress. He could smell potatoes burning quicker than anyone. When Barbara ran to the kitchen to tend her meal, Susan would watch the switchboard.

At age seven, Susan thought she was already old enough to take calls on the board. Every time she heard the alarm buzz, she would try to beat her mother back from the kitchen.

Chapter 7 - LIFE AROUND THE BOARD
Photograph by Hathaway

"Bob McKeen soon found that it would be a lot different working at the Hathaways'." He is pictured here with the first grandchild, Brian Hathaway, in 1970.

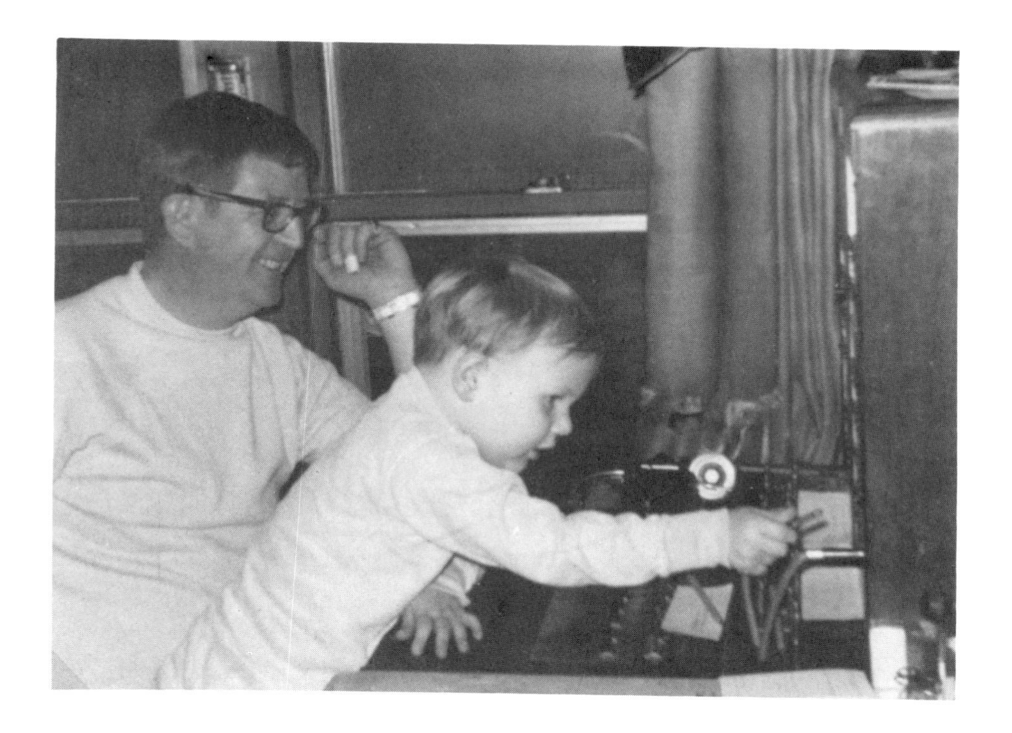

Chapter 7 - LIFE AROUND THE BOARD
Photograph by Hathaway

"On holidays the entire celebration was planned around the switchboard." Pictured L to R: Elden, Linda, 1969

"Operator," Barbara would say, out of breath.

Aunt Fanny Ross moved in with Barbara and Elden a couple of years before they bought the phone company. At that time they added a second story to the house with an attic above that so that there were enough bedrooms upstairs for everyone. Aunt Fanny was some help with the housework despite her age and health, but her failing eyesight made it difficult. However, she could still read to the children by hours, which Mike particularly liked.

Television had not made its way to Bryant Pond yet. Playing cards was a popular pastime in the evenings. Susan was a moody player, always wanting to be the winner. She discovered that she could watch the reflection of Bob's hand in the window as he sat at the switchboard.

"I don't understand how you are able to win so much," he always complained. Eventually he was able to catch on to her successful technique.

Then the switchboard would get busy and Susan would complain, "Darn, there's another call. It's getting so we have to stop every twenty minutes or so. I wish everybody would just go to bed."

"Now, Susan," Bob would say, "we have to answer them."

Bob got initiated to having kids around in a hurry. Susan used to patiently wait for him to leave the board for a moment to run to the bathroom or for a cup of coffee and then she would hide. She would jump out and yell "Boo!" as loud as she could to startle him. The result was a spilled coffee, a shaken Bob, and a delighted Susan.

Another aspect which changed abruptly was their social life. With Bob the only other telephone operator, Barbara had to be home every afternoon, and either she or Elden had to be there by 9 p.m. when Bob's second shift ended.

Fortunately Bob was agreeable to working some late evenings so that the Hathaways could attend Eastern Star. The meetings were once a month and were attended by a good part of the townspeople. An advantage was that the kids had a babysitter.

One evening around the kitchen table a short time after the board was installed, Barbara and Elden broke some exciting news to Mike and Susan.

"We're going to have another member of the family sometime in the spring," said Barbara. "I'm expecting a baby."

As Barbara grew larger and larger, the only place she could ride comfortably in the old milk wagon was behind the wheel driving.

Linda was born in April. Bob designed a birth announcement with a telephone company theme. Just as mother and child were to come home from the hospital, Mike came down with the flu and Barbara's grandmother Bennett died. Mike had to stay with his Hathaway grandparents until he got better, and Barbara missed the funeral, so it was a trying spell.

Linda fitted right in with the switchboard, spending most of her young life in the middle of all the activity. At night she slept in a crib in her parents' sleeping area. As soon as possible the living room was split in half, making a bedroom next to the office and a dining room off the kitchen.

Barbara nursed Linda at the board during afternoon feedings. When Linda reached a year old, her parents prepared a bedroom for her upstairs. However, at first she had trouble sleeping. It was too quiet up there.

In 1955 television arrived. All of a sudden soap operas, Cowboys and Indians, and wrestling matches filled the telephone office. The sound had to be carefully controlled so that the operators could hear the calls, but the TV set stayed on all day long.

Sometimes on a hot summer's night Barbara and Elden would escape to the front porch to enjoy the peace and quiet of the evening which was broken only by the sound of crickets' chirping or an occasional car passing.

"Remember when you used to come home from the railroad, and after dinner we'd walk down to the lake for a swim?" Barbara asked, thinking of the years before the switchboard.

"I know," Elden replied, wistfully puffing on his pipe.

"What time is it?" she asked.

"Almost nine."

"We've got to relieve Bob."

Out to the back room they returned - to blaring television, fighting kids, and a bustling switchboard.

Chapter 8

BUILDING A WHARF

Rumford Avenue starts its 20 mile journey to Rumford by joining Route 26 at the bottom of Merryfield Hill. This was the corner where Howard and Sylvia Judkins had their telephone office. For the first half mile the avenue's left side is bordered by a bog created years ago by beavers. Part of it was rumored to consist of bottomless quicksand. In fact, some of the old stories told of cattle being swallowed alive. There is also a smaller bog on the right side of the street. Both sides have brooks flowing through them on the way to Lake Christopher.

Wildlife frequents the wet habitat, including ducks, heron, mud hens, muskrat, deer, and even an occasional moose. The larger bog was dammed up in the early 1900's in an attempt to grow cranberries, but the venture didn't succeed. Later the fire department repaired the earthen dam to hold water in case of fire on the avenue. For years fishing was not allowed in the bogs because they were tributaries to the lake. The small bog filled with waterlilies in the summer and was a very popular neighborhood skating spot during the winter.

In their preteen years Mike and his friends spent a lot of time on the waters of Lake Christopher, North Pond, and South Pond, spincasting and trolling for bass and pickerel. When the law changed to permit fishing in the bog, the boys thought it would be fun to try their luck. A likely spot seemed to be down at the bottom of the 40 foot bank right in back of the telephone office.

"Dad, will you help us build a wharf?" Mike asked. They wanted to be able to stand a few feet offshore so they could cast without getting hung up in the trees.

"I guess so, but we'll have to scrounge around for some boards, and most important, some posts that we can drive into the bottom." He thought a moment. "I've got an old telephone pole that might just serve the purpose."

With the help of the neighborhood kids, Elden set out to engineer the building of the fishing pier. The boys passed the boards down the bank to the water's edge, and Mike, using a one-man cross-cut saw, was delegated to cut down the old cedar telephone pole and junk it up into the required lengths. The project progressed nicely until Elden found he still needed another post before it could be finished.

"Mike," he yelled up to the top of the bank, "saw down the old cedar clothesline in back of the house." Barbara hadn't used it since they built the addition for the telephone office. "I think that will work out just fine," he concluded.

Mike got the saw ready and went to work, thinking of the fun he would soon have fishing from the new wharf.

From down at the foot of the banking, Elden could hear a saw as it chewed through the soft wood. His eye was drawn to the nearby pole with all the telephone lines leading into the office.

"Are you sure you're cutting down the clothesline post?" he anxiously hollered up, knowing his son sometimes did not pay attention to close detail.

By this time Mike was already half way through. He stopped and looked up. A sickening feeling hit his stomach. There above him towered the old cedar telephone pole that held every incoming line in the Bryant Pond phone system! Five feet away the old clothesline post stood straight without a saw mark.

"Dad, I'm afraid I've made a little mistake," a nervous Mike called down the bank. "The telephone pole looked just like the clothesline, and I, ah, started to cut the wrong one."

Elden looked up in disbelief. If that pole went over, it could disconnect the whole town! He hurried up the bank to take a closer look.

"It's a good thing I stopped you before that pole fell over!" Work on the wharf was suspended.

"Get me a couple of 2x4s!" Elden ordered after surveying the situation. Mike was able to find some, and his dad nailed them to the pole, hoping to provide a brace.

"Well, I guess you've got a job to do for the next couple of days," Elden told Mike. "I want you to dig a hole right beside the pole you tried to saw down. I'll have to make arrangements to get a new one so we can transfer the lines onto it. I just hope we don't get any strong wind before we get it in place!"

Mike went to work. The ground was very "bony" and he had to lift out many rocks, some as large as pumpkins. He dug and he dug until the hole was deep enough to support the new pole. By the next Saturday the crew, plus one or two of the neighborhood boys, assembled to raise it into place. Mike filled in the leftover dirt and rocks and tamped around the bottom to keep the top from swaying. Elden spent several hours changing over the lines. Mike then finished cutting down the old pole, and it became part of the wharf.

The new pole stayed in place for the length of time that Barbara

Chapter 8 - BUILDING A WHARF
Photograph by Jack Quinn, Lewiston Daily Sun, 1973

"The old cedar telephone pole held every incoming line in the Bryant Pond phone system."

and Elden owned the telephone company. For a few years Mike got in a lot of hours fishing off the wharf down the bank behind the telephone office.

Chapter 9

TALES OF THE OLD MILK WAGON

Having worked on the railroad all his adult life, Elden had never felt the need to own a car. Now that he had to get to telephone line troubles at a moment's notice, he had to learn how to drive. In order to practice his driving, he had to have someone with a valid license ride with him. Every time he was called out to make a repair, he would have to call up a neighbor. This was often at some odd hour of the night. As his skill increased, so did his confidence, and he sometimes took chances leaving the office without a legal license.

Barbara, on the other hand, had learned as a teenager, purchasing her license in a drug store. She used to work for and drive around Bryant Pond's well-known summer resident, the daughter of President Rutherford B. Hayes. Mrs. Hayes, as she was known by her maiden name, took such a liking to Barbara that she paid her way to Gould Academy in Bethel, Maine.

Knowing that the old Plymouth was not going to fit the bill, Elden started looking for another vehicle. It did not take him long to find a 1941 International Oakhurst milk delivery wagon. It also proved to be a finicky old truck with a four-speed floor shift, and a single seat for the driver. It had a metal bench along both walls of its open interior.

When the Hathaways purchased it, it still wore the name and colors of the dairy. Elden painted the truck a dark green, and Barbara made seat cushions for the benches.

On Eastern Star night Elden would unload all the telephone equipment from the back, and the couple would pick up the whole neighborhood and take them to the meeting. It was quite a sight to see all those men in their tuxedos and ladies in long gowns piling in and out of the old green milk wagon.

The truck worked out very well for telephone line repairs, especially when the temperature was below freezing. With its open interior the crew could pull the lines right inside, protecting them from the cold.

Once the wire was fixed, Elden would call Central on an Army field phone to see if the parties on the line could be reached. The Army field phone came in a leather carrying case with a shoulder strap. Two wires with clips on the ends connected the phone to either bare wire or the copper sleeves. The phone had its own crank and batteries for talking.

In this manner, he would call a customer like Frank Bean on the Gore Road. "Hello, Frank, this is Elden," he would thankfully say to his customer. "Sounds like your phone is working again."

"Well, that's great," Frank replied. "I didn't even know it was out of order!" In those early days, that was often the case. Many of the customers were not used to a lot of talk on the phone. The operator would often know that there was trouble on the line long before they did.

The side doors on the wagon opened by sliding back and forth and were quite hard to close. It took all of Barbara's might to get the task done. One day she drove to Locke Mills to pick up some favors for an Eastern Star supper that evening. On the way home she hit a bump in the road which caused the side door to fly open. Out spilled all the favors. They scattered all over the roadside. She quickly pulled to a stop. She was very pregnant at the time and created quiet a spectacle running back and forth across the highway. Several passing cars stopped to help her retrieve the elusive favors as they slipped along with the wind.

- - - - - - - - - -

During the first Christmas school vacation that they owned the company, Elden hired his nephew Dean Bennett and Fred Farnum to build a new line over Rowe Hill. It was a remote section of the telephone company territory, and the only service to that area was one of the two remaining independently owned "farmers lines". It was sadly in disrepair, and none of the owners wanted to rebuild it. Some of them had approached Elden, requesting that he consider constructing a new Bryant Pond Telephone Company line.

Mike went along to help in any way he could, mostly by pulling the Army field wire along the road by hand. He struggled to haul up to a half mile of the wire as it uncoiled off the reel. Fred sometimes had to wade through deep snow when the power poles left the side of the road. Fred and Dean had to use trees where the poles weren't available.

The winter snows were deep, and the dirt road was little more than one lane. It wound up and down over several steep hills and a deep valley so narrow that the milk wagon had to build up a lot of momentum. Fred would have to speed downhill in order to make it up the other side. Late one afternoon, as he was driving the truck toward home, Fred took his eyes off the road for a moment. He was attempting to light his pipe.

"Look out!" he yelled as the wheels jumped out of the rut and the wagon was pulled straight towards a snowbank.

CRASH! Tools and wire slid forward and scattered over the truck's interior. The occupants sat there in stunned silence.

"Well, I guess everyone's OK," Dean said after checking with Mike and Fred. "Let's see about damage."

The front of the old milk wagon was buried in the snowbank. They went to work shoveling, and fortunately a passerby carrying a chain in his vehicle gave them a pull and got the truck back onto the road. They arrived back in the office after dark a couple of hours late.

Barbara's mother, Cora Bennett, was visiting and was anxiously waiting for a ride home. She didn't like to ride in cars, and with the boys late, she was fretting more than usual. Elden got behind the wheel of the old milk wagon to take her back to Locke Mills. Shortly after they left the dooryard, he met a car and moved to the edge of the road so that there would be room to pass. The truck leaped towards the woods.

"Elden, quit fooling around," Cora scolded him. "If you aren't careful, we'll both be killed!"

"I'm not fooling. This thing is acting strange," he said.

The wagon continued its erratic behavior, leaping towards the woods or the center of the road. Elden headed straight to Tyler's Garage in the center of town. By now Cora was as white as a sheet.

"Looks like you got a bent tie rod," Harold drawled as he looked under the truck. "What'd you hit anyways?"

"The boys got stuck over on Rowe Hill. Can you straighten it out?" Elden asked anxiously.

"Well, I can make it a lot better than it is now," he returned. He sledge-hammered it back in place, and it never bothered again. From then on, as long as Barbara and Elden owned the vehicle, Cora rode in it as little as possible.

Mike never trusted the old milk wagon again either. For one thing, it was very hard to shift, and the gear box whined so that he was convinced it would explode. He would hold his breath every time his father pushed down on the throttle in first or second gear. After the Rowe Hill incident, he always rode braced for an accident, holding onto the sides of the truck for dear life.

As Elden continued to work for the railroad, the milk wagon also came in handy during the winter to haul the section crew about to shovel out crossings and switches. It was much more pleasant than riding over the rails on the unheated and partially open motor car.

One particularly cold day the crew headed for the shelter of the truck as quitting time neared. Pete Wing, who was later to work for the telephone company after his retirement from the railroad, was the last to get in. He always had trouble with the truck's sliding door.

"Pete, let me give you a hand," Elden said, wanting to keep the cold air out. "It's not that hard once you know the combination." He reached over and gave the door a yank. "See, it was just as easy as that."

They started back to the car-house.

After a short silence, Pete said, "Elden, would you mind opening the door again?"

"But I just got it shut," he protested.

"I know, but I got my ear caught in it!"

Sure enough, one of Pete's big cauliflower ears was slammed shut in the door. The rest of the crew doubled over with laughter as Elden pulled the truck over to the side of the road and released Pete's ear. Fortunately, no serious harm was done, but poor Pete had a hard time living that incident down.

As the truck got older and the family grew, Barbara and Elden traded the old milk wagon for a 1950 Ford "woody" stationwagon. It often carried the whole Little League baseball team to games that Elden coached.

Chapter 10

LEARNING TO HUNT TELEPHONE TROUBLES

When Barbara and Elden purchased the company, most of the lines were constructed with surplus World War II Army field wire that was designed to be run along the ground to connect military outposts with command headquarters. It was not manufactured to last a long time, and by 1950 the cotton covering known as insulation was beginning to rot. The least amount of friction would break the fabric and allow the bared metal strands inside to touch each other. Sometimes moisture would act as a conductor and cause a short circuit when a spurt of electricity was generated by the ring of a phone. A call would not be able to get beyond the point of the resistance.

Elden would have to spend countless hours climbing poles, wading through deep snow and inspecting the places where wire was rubbed by tree limbs. As undesirable as the older open wire lines were, at least the crosses and tangles could easily be seen and separated. Howard Judkins had shown him how to use the ohmmeter that came with the telephone equipment. It was a small oblong box with a metal gauge connected to a line by two caps on the ends of its lead wires.

"First you want to take a reading from the office. The rig reads about fifteen points a mile. If the needle says thirty, then you want to head out a couple miles or so. When you pick a spot to check the wire, you've got to cut one side of the line so you know which direction to hunt for the trouble. When the needle registers 'zero', you know you are very close to where those bare wires are touching each other," Howard advised Elden.

"Maybe I can make it work without cutting the line," Elden convinced himself, wanting to save on the extra work of splicing the wires back together. He was thinking about what a miserable job that would be in the wind.

One cold day, shortly after the company had moved to the Hathaways, the Gore Road line, which was one of the longest and most populated (about 18 customers), went out of order. Elden headed off to fix it, and following the direction of the ohmmeter, located a possible area where the trouble might very well be. It was at the top of Cemetery Hill where there were no power poles. The old field wire was spread along a fence which wound its way through thick underbrush to the bottom of the hill a quarter mile below. There was about four feet of snow on the ground, and he sure didn't want to plow through it if he didn't have to.

"I don't think the problem is in there," Elden convinced himself, "and besides, it won't take long to check further down the road where I know the wind blows really hard." He just didn't want to cut the line and waste all that time splicing it back together.

He continued looking, climbing pole after pole, until his legs were just about worn out. Finally he gave in and cut the line, checked with the ohmmeter, and it said the trouble was far back the other way. To the top of Cemetery Hill he went again, and this time he tested the line. It read 'zero'.

"Well I'll be," he muttered. Off into the deep snow he went, but only a few feet, before he found the break in the insulation that he was looking for. Taking out his tape, he carefully covered each bare wire.

"I guess from now on, I'll follow the ohmmeter instead of my nose," he told himself as he drove home.

Barbara and Elden both worried about breakdowns on the lines. In the winter when the cold reached well below freezing, the townspeople would push their woodstoves to the limit trying to keep their houses warm. Their only contact with the fire department was by phone. The Hathaways particularly dreaded windy or snowy nights when the chances of a disaster were higher.

One evening during a cornmeal snowstorm, the Rowe Hill line went out of order. Cornmeal snow is very grainy, almost like ice pellets. A few inches of accumulation makes walking or driving very difficult. Elden left as soon as he arrived home from the railroad. He could not make it up to the top of the first steep grade with the old milk wagon. Putting on his safety belt and spurs, he grabbed a flashlight, a handful of wire, an ax, his field phone, and all the tools he could fit in his belt and set out on the two mile hike to look for the trouble. He found the old iron lines tangled several times on the way to the first customer's house where an elderly lady was ill. Drenched to the bone by the time he arrived, he knocked at the door.

"What are you doing over here?" the owner said in a surprised tone as he peered out into the storm, spitting out what seemed to be a quart of tobacco juice into the fresh snow.

"Well, your phone was out of order, but I think I've got it fixed."

"If I was you, I'd have waited 'til a better day."

"I knew your mother was sick, and I couldn't rest until it was working," Elden replied.

With that he went inside and tried the phone. It was working once more. Then he walked the long road back to the milk wagon, and finally got home to his supper. Over the years, that kind of dedication made Elden and Barbara dear to the hearts of their customers.

- - - - - - - - - -

Dean Bennett was still in high school when he started helping Elden on the telephone lines. He was Barbara's nephew, the oldest son of Donald and Elsie Bennett. The family lived in Locke Mills, next to Barbara's parents.

"Uncle Putt, had you just as soon come here a minute?" Dean called to Elden. They were working just out of sight of each other on the Indian Pond line which connected to the Rowe Hill line.

"Be right there," he replied. Elden took the time to finish up what he was doing, another five minutes or so, then walked over to give his nephew a hand. There he found Dean hanging onto the telephone pole for dear life. He had climbed it with a ladder, but the ladder had twisted and fallen out from under him, tangling up his feet in the process. Dean held onto the pole with his hands and arms until he kicked his feet free so that he could maintain his grip. Elden quickly got the ladder back under him so that he could safely get down.

"You should have hollered 'help'," Elden told him.

"Well, I didn't think you'd take so long as you did. Besides, I was holding on too tight to yell."

Dean was a good sport and often the brunt of Elden's practical jokes, like the time they found a break in the telephone line on the side of a house. He climbed a short ladder to fix the trouble while Elden quietly hooked up his field phone to the protector box where he could watch his nephew. Each time Dean went to splice the wires together, Elden would turn the crank. Dean would drop the line.

"What's the matter?" Elden asked.

"I get a shock when I put the wires together!"

"I don't believe it," Elden said. "Telephone lines don't carry electricity."

And each time Dean would try to make the connection, Elden would turn the crank again.

Finally, the teenager realized what his uncle was doing.

"Oh, I see! You're just trying to be funny!"

They both had a good laugh as they headed back to the office.

- - - - - - - - - -

"Elden, we've had a request for a phone way in on the back side of North Pond," Barbara told him one night after supper. "They need it as soon as possible."

"We don't have any poles or wire in there," he said. "It's going to take time to build a line."

"Is there anything you can do to get them temporary service?" she asked.

"Well, I could run the wire on the ground and then put it up on trees and set poles where I need them afterwards."

"They would really appreciate it."

"Well, then I guess we could hook them up this weekend."

By Saturday night he had the customer connected with a mile of wire propped up on trees and bushes. By the middle of the next week he got a report that the line was out of order already, so he headed off after work on the railroad to repair it. He traced the line's path through the woods, toward the cabin, when all of a sudden it disappeared.

"Would you look at this!" he said to himself. "It's broken clean off." He hunted for the other end.

"Well, I'll be!"

There in the ground were the hoof prints of a large bull moose. It had gotten its antlers tangled up in the wire and dragged away a large section of the line. Elden put the wire up in the trees as soon as he had the time.

- - - - - - - - - -

A lovely estate on the outlet cove of the Little Androscoggin River on Lake Christopher was owned by Pennsylvania millionairess Mrs. Hall. Members of her family spent time there during the summer. One rainy evening she called the "cottage" from her home in Pennsylvania and was very disturbed when the line went dead in the middle of her conversation.

"Can you fix that right away?" she requested.

Out into the downpour Elden went, getting soaked to the skin. Not far from the mansion he discovered a small tree lying on the broken wire. A beaver had gnawed through the trunk.

Chapter 11

WAKE UP, ELDEN

Barbara usually went to bed earlier than her husband. She would wake early in the morning to tend the board because it was a favorite time for businessmen to make their calls if they were going to be away from their office all day.

It was Elden's part of the bargain to tend the switchboard late at night. By ten o'clock most of the town was in bed, and late calls were

Map of the Byrant Pond Telephone Company Territory

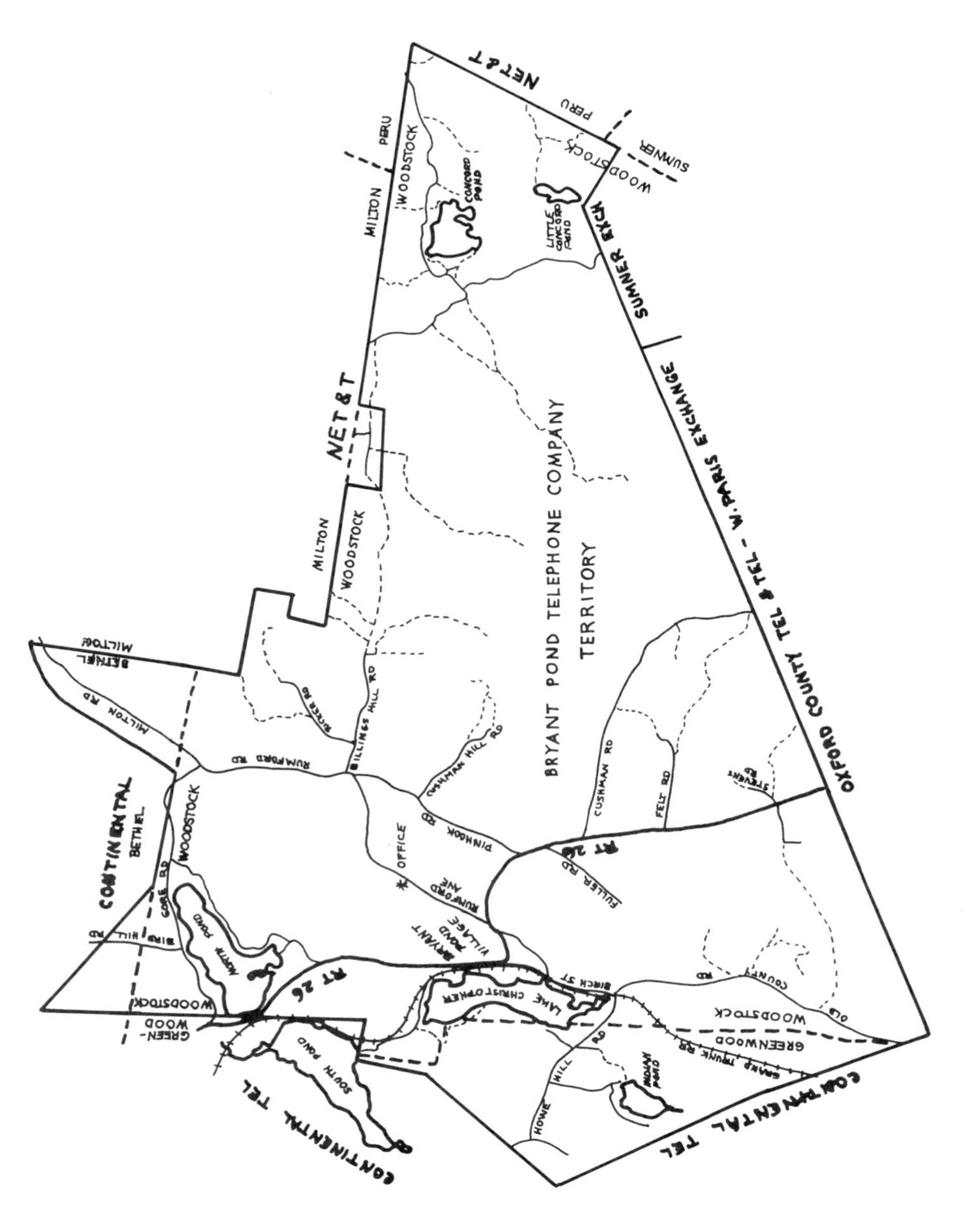

usually emergencies. Once the board had quieted down and calling had stopped for the night, Elden would put the night alarm on and head for bed. Whenever it sounded, he would jump out of bed to answer it. There was one minor problem though. Once he got to sleep, he was very hard to wake up.

"Elden, wake up!" Barbara would have to say.

The urgency of the night alarm woke the entire household, except Elden.

"Elden!" Barbara would say, trying to push him on his way with her feet, "Are you awake?"

Finally he would stagger out of bed and feel his way toward the switchboard.

"Elden, is that you?" The young woman sounded anxious on the other end of the line. "My little girl seems to have come down with a fever. Probably the flu that's going around, but she's quite hot. Can you get me Doc Nangle in West Paris?"

"Let's try," Elden responded, still half asleep, as he rang the Norway operator.

"West Paris, please."

"Hello," the tired voice answered.

"Thank goodness! Dr. Nangle, my little girl is sick. I think she has the flu. What should I do?" she asked as she told him her story.

The doctor gave her advice and said he would come by in the morning if she wasn't improved.

Back to bed went Elden.

"It's ringing again! Elden, are you awake?"

"uuh..."

"Hello, sir. I woke up, and my clock has stopped. Can you tell me what time it is?"

"Lady, it's ten minutes of four," Elden mumbled.

"Oh, thank you. I was afraid I'd overslept."

Back to bed.

"Elden, can't you hear the alarm? Remember, it's your night to tend it," said Barbara.

"Elden, there's been a bad auto accident on Whale's Back Road. Can you get help?"

That was the type of call the operators always dreaded. Elden was now fully awake, but calmly handling the situation.

"I'll connect you with Andrews' Ambulance, and you can tell him the location."

An anxious moment until Norway answered - "We have an emergency! Please connect us to Andrews."

Andrews answered.

Elden listened to the call and then contacted Doc Nangle again.

"We have a bad auto accident Doc. Can you get here as soon as possible? Andrews is on the way."

Next he notified Stephens Memorial Hospital, the Sheriff's Department, the Town Constable, and Tyler's Garage.

The switchboard was now humming with activity as dawn's first light began to illuminate the sky. Barbara put the coffee on. The aroma floated into the office.

"Elden, your breakfast is ready. I'll take over so you can eat and get ready to go to work on the railroad."

Another night on the switchboard had ended.

- - - - - - - - - -

When Elden was left alone with the switchboard at night, sometimes nothing would wake him. One year Susan had an early morning paper route, and while she was away at summer camp, Barbara and Mike had to keep up the deliveries.

"I think I can hear the alarm," Mike said one morning as they returned home.

"Oh no!" Barbara said as she opened the door and rushed for the board.

"Operator - hello - operator!" She hurriedly checked out the half dozen downed drops. No one answered her. They had all given up waiting.

"Oh, are you back already?" Elden said as Barbara woke him. "Everything's quiet here."

"Oh, Elden! You slept right through the alarm again!" She shook her head.

The last straw occurred several years later when everyone except Elden had gone to a night of theater in Brunswick. The operators at Norway became concerned when they couldn't raise Bryant Pond. They took emergency action.

"Hello, Sheriff's Department? I can't get through to the Bryant Pond telephone operator. We've never had a problem like this before. Can you find out if anything's wrong?"

"We'll send a deputy right up to check."

When the deputy arrived at the Hathaways', the house was dark except for the dim light by the board.

As the deputy approached he saw that the screen door seemed to be broken. "I'd better call for a backup," he told himself. A second deputy arrived, and Rumford Avenue became aglow with flashing blue lights.

"There's no answer at the door, and the telephone alarm is ringing. Do you think there has been foul play?"

Guns drawn, they prepared to enter the house.

At that very moment Barbara turned onto Rumford Avenue, arriving home from the theater. "What's going on?" Linda asked her mother as they drove up the street. "Look! It's at the house!"

They reached the yard just as the sheriffs were about to pry the door open.

The officers filled them in. Barbara unlocked the door, and they found Elden asleep in bed.

"That does it!" she said. "We can't trust you to stay alone at night with the switchboard anymore!"

Chapter 12

BOB McKEEN

In the early 1940's when Bob McKeen was in high school, he and three other friends used to spend evenings doing homework by phone. One of them was the night telephone operator. There were virtually no interruptions from other callers.

In 1946 after serving in the U.S. Army, Bob went to work for the phone company. The Meserves were in the process of getting a divorce at the time, and he was left alone to tend the board day and night as the owners went their separate ways. There were only twelve telephone lines at that time.

Within a couple of months he found himself tending the switchboard for new owners of the company, Howard and Sylvia Judkins. The Judkins rented their upstairs apartment to the McKeen family. This made it very convenient for Bob to go to work. They had given him an opportunity to purchase the telephone business at one time for $1500, but he was advised by several people not to do it because they considered it a poor investment which "had no future."

When Barbara and Elden took ownership, they knew nothing about the telephone business, and Bob became indispensable. He had to make the adjustment from peace and quiet to constant confusion of fighting kids and blaring radios. He was an excellent artist and did a lot of freelance posters for various town organizations as well as the yearly telephone company Christmas cards.

He also did most of the telephone company bookkeeping, which at first was very simple. Once a month he and Barbara would make a list of all the toll calls and do the billings. They started at 8 a.m. and would have all the bills ready for mailing by noon when the R.F.D. postman came. By the end of the Hathaways' ownership, the monthly bookkeeping duties had turned into a daily task. Bob spent his entire morning shift working on billings.

- - - - - - - - - -

"You're a male telephone operator?" Those words often greeted him as he answered incoming toll calls from out-of-state. He was a novelty in a woman's world and very popular with the girls at the nearby Norway office. He occasionally found time to make his way to the living room to play piano for the kids who listened spellbound.

Before Elden got his license Bob sometimes had to accompany him while he hunted for line trouble, leaving Barbara to tend the board. He knew every customer well and their peculiarities.

He remembered one emergency call.

Chapter 12 - BOB McKEEN
Original Christmas Card

"He was an excellent artist and did a lot of freelance posters...as well as the yearly telephone company Christmas cards."

"Can you get some help? My wife has fallen down outside, and I can't get her up."

Bob called for assistance. The trip to Milton took almost half an hour. When the rescue workers arrived, the woman was still down. Her husband had forgotten to report that the reason why she couldn't get up was that she was too drunk to stand.

- - - - - - - - - -

At 5:20 one night, shortly after Bob started his evening shift, the eight line dropped. It was his father, Stowell's Mill superintendent, who was working late.

"Get Kirk Stowell (the mill owner) and the fire department! The mill is on fire!"

Bob went into action. He rang the fire department 10-5. The call was answered by Chief Harold Tyler from his home 10-3.

"I'm leaving for the station to blow the fire horn and get the engine ready to move," he responded. "You call some of the firefighters, and my wife will call the rest."

One by one the volunteers were contacted, most of them before the horn sounded its alarm.

"Fire at Stowell's Mill!" The message was repeated over and over. No need for other conversation. Once the horn blew, the board came alive with callers wanting to know where the fire was.

It was located within a thousand feet of the fire station. A large crowd gathered on the road across the tracks from the mill. The firemen were quick to respond. At first just smoke spewed from the old wooden structure.

"Call Greenwood and West Paris. We need help!" Harold yelled over the phone. The flames started to break through the roof, and soon the night was filled with a reddish glow. Even with the help of the neighboring departments, the mill was totally destroyed, putting many of the townspeople out of work. The fire fighters tried valiantly, and succeeded in keeping the blaze from spreading to other buildings at the mill site and on the street. It had been the busiest and most traumatic night of Bob's career. He completely lost his voice.

"Let me relieve you," Elden said as he returned from the fire scene. Bob went down to see the aftermath of the tragedy that he had worked so hard through.

The town pulled together to aid those who lost their jobs while the mill was rebuilt.

Chapter 13

BIRD HILL

Each telephone company in the State of Maine had a specific area in which it was allowed to provide service. In the early part of the 1900's Maine had many of these independent ventures. Usually they started as a community effort but eventually gave way to a single owner. By the 1950's larger companies such as New England Telephone had swallowed up many of the smaller ones. N.E.T. owned large chunks of territories.

Bryant Pond's area was approximately 100 square miles, bordered by Rumford on the West, Oxford on the South, and the Bethel Phone Companies to the East and North. Each of these territories was regulated by the Maine Public Utilities Commission.

Customers had to receive the service provided in their designated areas unless that right was waived by their telephone company. Because these territories had specific boundaries, neighbors who had the misfortune to live on the line were forced to use different telephone companies. Therefore, they had to pay toll charges for calling next door.

Bryant Pond had one exception, a dial line which ran all the way from Mann's Mill and the owner's residence nearby to the West Paris Phone Company. This agreement had been formed years before. As a result the mill was able to call toll free to customers in the next territory. Addie Mann had both a West Paris dial phone and Bryant Pond crank phone in her home.

Bird Hill was a remote section of the Bethel Telephone Company. It was located in the township of Greenwood on the back side of a mountain near the town of Locke Mills, abutting the Bryant Pond Telephone Company's territory. The owner of the farmhouse on the top of the mountain decided he wanted to have a telephone. The Mann's power line went through the Bryant Pond territory as Bethel did not want the expense of providing telephone service. Bethel gladly waived this portion of their territory to Bryant Pond.

The wire had to be run over several miles of power poles. The power line followed a logging road for a while and then cut its own path up the steep terrain to the top of the mountain.

Having existing poles was a definite savings in building costs, and as often as they could, the Hathaways rented poles from the Central Maine Power Company. Not only were the poles already in the ground, the trees and brush were kept cleared underneath them. Most of the poles were very hard western fir, completely impregnated with creosote preservative to prevent rot.

When C.M.P. poles weren't available, Elden would scrounge around for old power poles that still had life. When these weren't available, he would buy softwood cedar ones from local farmers who cut them from their woodlots. Cedar was one of the most rot resistant types of native New England wood.

Getting a climbing spur to go into a hard western fir was like trying to get a foothold on a rock wall. Sometimes the pointed steel tips would only penetrate a quarter of an inch. Needless to say, the climber felt very insecure. Veteran telephone men preferred using old spurs with filed-down points for the harder poles so their feet would be closer to the wood.

To set a pole, a hole of four to five feet deep had to be dug in the usually very rocky ground. It took a lot of time to work the rocks free to reach the desired depth. The tools Elden used for this task included short and long handled spades, a long iron bar and a 10 foot spoon-type shovel. This item made it possible to lift small amounts of loose dirt and rocks out when the hole got deep.

After it was finished, a strong-backed crew of four or five men would "walk" the pole upright until it was in its resting place. Some of the heavier poles needed the help of the truck. A rope would be attached from the bumper to the top of the pole. As the top began to raise toward the sky, a couple of the crew would grab "pick poles" (long poles with sharp iron points) to guide its direction. Sometimes it was impossible to rent or set poles. Then Elden would have to resort to trees.

Construction expenses were shared by the subscriber and the telephone company. The Maine Public Utilities Commission had a formula for setting this cost. Once an agreement was reached with the Bethel Telephone Company and the customer, Elden built the line to the top of Bird Hill.

- - - - - - - - -

As luck would have it, the line on Bird Hill decided to go out of order one wintry day. The ground was covered with a couple feet of lightly crusted snow, too thick for snowshoes and too thin to hold body weight. Elden set out alone on foot in search for the trouble.

The hike through the remote countryside was exhausting. He worked his way into the woods, and after traveling a couple of miles found a spot that looked like it might be the problem. It was up on one of the power company's western fir poles.

His legs were weak from wading through the deep snow. He could feel them shake as he started his climb. Slowly he worked his way up toward the telephone line. When he got there, he hooked his safety belt and proceeded to do his work. After he completed it, he leaned forward to unhook himself when both feet lost their grip.

Elden started to fall. He desperately tried to break his momentum by hugging the pole and jabbing at it wildly with his spurs. Just a few feet from the bottom, one spur finally found a grip in the wood. He came to a sudden halt with a neck-snapping crunch. There he hung in mid-air, secured only by one foot and the safety strap which he had been trying to unbuckle when he fell. As he tried to recover his breath, he slowly checked himself to see what the damage might be. He didn't feel anything seriously wrong. Except for a few bruises and a stiff neck, he was all right.

"What am I doing out here in the woods alone?" he scolded himself. "If I'd been hurt, it would have taken someone several hours to find me, and by then I could have frozen to death." Slowly he managed to work his way down the rest of the pole.

"I guess I've learned a lesson," he thought. "Next time I will make sure I have someone with me when I go out on a remote telephone line repair."

Chapter 14

PETE & PUTT

Elden's father Rupert had been a railroad man all his life. He started on the extra gangs and worked his way up to an assistant road master before he retired. He was known for his lack of mechanical ability, and many railroad men thought the fact that his motor car would run at all was an "absolute miracle". He never did any maintenance on it. He just started the engine and went. For anyone else, it wouldn't have run at all. "Putt", as he was nicknamed, just kept putting along day after day, always reaching his destination.

Pete Wing worked for the section crew that maintained the track along the rail line that included the town of Woodstock and the village of Bryant Pond. He was a thin wiry man with little formal education. He had little ambition, and he enjoyed getting on Putt's nerves. However, he did have a driver's license, and Putt didn't.

Pete fancied himself some sort of magician, always doing little tricks with loose coins and cigarettes. His favorite pastime when not working was sitting in front of his small house near Stowell's Mill, playing his harmonica and watching the traffic go by. Both men retired from the railroad within a short time of each other.

At that time Elden was working full time for the railroad during the day and repairing telephone lines at night. He had all he could do to stay up with the repair work, to say nothing of running the urgently needed new lines.

He got an idea. Now that his father and Pete were at loose ends, maybe they could give him a hand. Mike, now in high school, was also available in the summer. He was exceptionally big for his age and could do the bulk of the heavy work. A deal was struck. Rupert, who was very lame from his years on the railroad, would be the foreman in charge. Pete would drive the truck and be the climber. Mike, who knew more about telephones, would do the heavy ground work and some ladder climbing. They would work about twenty hours a week.

"The first job I want to do," Elden told his crew, "is to put a cable up from the office to Pinhook and over Whales Back. When that's done you can upgrade the lines over the Gore out to Milton Plantation. I've got a chance at a good buy on Army surplus five-pair cable. You'll either have to tape it or tie it with rope to an iron wire carrying strand in order to hold it up. It won't support itself. You'll also have to put in some cedar telephone poles where the old line is hitched to trees. I've got some being cut by one of the farmers out towards the Gore. You can pick them right up in his barnyard."

The crew went to work. They scoured the telephone territory for old unused iron wire, and cut it down from abandoned telephone lines which were often long overgrown with trees and underbrush. Mike climbed one pole ten feet or so and cut the iron wire. All of a sudden it gave way beneath him. It had rotted off at its base.

"Look out!" he yelled as he rode the pole to the ground, jumping clear at the last moment.

Chapter 14 - PUTT & PETE
Photograph by Hathaway

"Rupert (Putt) would be the foreman... Pete would drive..."
Pictured L to R: Putt, Pete.

"Wow, that was a close one!" Pete said. "I'm lucky I wasn't under you when you fell!"

Most of the time Mike and Pete climbed by ladder, hooking their safety belts to help keep them from sliding around the poles. Putt would pull on the cable from the ground, getting it up in the air as much as possible. Mike or Pete, whoever was up the pole, would hook a come-a-long onto the iron wire that supported the cable and pull up the slack. Neither of them enjoyed heights, and every time Putt would yank on the come-a-long rope, the pole would sway under the added strain of the cable's weight.

"Hey! That's high enough!" Mike would yell down.

"No it's not!" Putt would holler up, and he would yank on the rope again. Mike held on for dear life.

At the encouragement of the older men, Mike decided to learn to climb with spurs. There were some places where a ladder would be almost impossible to carry. Taking a deep breath, he put on a safety belt and spurs and set out to give it a try. He chose an old cedar pole, nice and soft for his spurs to sink into. It was a pole near the telephone office. When he got up five feet or so, he stopped to rest. At that time he weighed a good 285 pounds. His weight pushed the points of the spurs so deep into the wood that his feet became stuck. Try as hard as he might, he couldn't get them loose.

"Hey! I need some help!" he yelled to Pete and Putt. "I can't get my feet out of the pole! I'm stuck!" Five feet off the ground seemed like a hundred feet to him.

Pete and Putt each grabbed a foot and lifted upward as hard as they could. Just about that time Elden arrived home.

"What on earth are you guys doing!" he asked as he watched the two old men straining to free Mike.

"He's stuck!" Pete yelled back. "We're trying to get him loose."

"Boy, I wish I had a camera!" Elden roared as he sat back and watched, tears of laughter running down his cheeks.

Working on one leg at a time, Putt and Pete finally got Mike back down to the ground. After that Mike stuck with the ladder.

Chapter 15

DON'T YOU WANT TO SWITCH TO DIAL?

The pressure to change the old hand crank system over to dial started almost as soon as the Hathaways bought the company.

"Elden, there's a gentleman from the R.E.A. Federal Loan Program calling to see if we would like to talk about getting a loan to change over to dial," Bob informed him one day.

"Well, I'm willing to listen," he responded, "but it will have to be a mighty good offer." They set a date to meet. I'm sure you realize that most of the small companies around you are making the move," the loan expert stated as he started his presentation. "Now is the time to update your system and change with the times."

He spent the day going over the company's books, analyzing its size and projected growth.

"Of course you will want to start with everything new. You'll have to have better wire and install cable to replace those big bunches of lines. The phones that are now in service are worthless. The best thing to do with them is tear them all out and throw them on the dump. You won't need a switchboard anymore as all your out-of-town calls will be handled by the Norway toll center. You'll save quite a bit as far as salaries go."

"Well, it sounds interesting," Elden answered, "but what is all this going to cost? Can we afford it?"

"I feel that for a loan of around $300,000 you could put yourself in quite a nice dial system."

"$300,000!" Elden said unbelievingly. "How on earth could we make payments on a loan like that!"

"The interest rate is very low, currently at three percent, and you can have up to fifty years to pay it off. Of course you will also have to petition the Public Utility Commission for a large rate increase. Your customers are paying the lowest phone bills in the state. They will actually be underwriting the expense of the changeover. And by the way", he concluded, "you'll also need to get a new phone truck. I figured that into the loan amount we'll give you."

Elden was speechless. He remained silent for a moment or so.

"You mean I can get $300,000 from you with fifty years to pay it back, and if I work it right, I can pass all the costs right on to my subscribers?"

"That's right. Aren't you glad that we made this service available to you? Your company will be set for years to come. You will of course have to have an engineering study made before the loan is approved."

"How much will that cost?"

"Probably about $5000."

"What happens if they don't approve the loan after the study?"

"Well, of course you'll have to pay for that anyway."

"Now I'm not against dial phones," Elden stated, "and I know that sooner or later we'll have to make the changeover, but Barbara and I don't want to saddle our children with a debt that will last for fifty years. We also don't feel right asking all the good people in town, most of whom work hard for the little money they do make, to dig so deep into their pockets. Those fancy new dial phones could cause quite a hardship on them," Elden continued.

"You are right about the phone wires. They are old and will have to be replaced regardless of whether we have magneto or dial. I think the best thing for us to do is fix up what we have first, and then look at changing over in a few years. Besides we don't have $5000 for a study."

"Well, you know the interest rates and costs are going up, and a chance like this won't happen again."

"Yes, I know, but now is not the time to make the change."

"Well, if we can help you in the future, please call."

"Maybe we're doing the wrong thing," Elden said to Barbara later, " but I sure feel good about the decision we made!"

The R.E.A. contacted Elden once every year or so for a while afterwards but eventually gave up.

Most of the other companies in the state made the changes to dial. Whenever they did, Elden would purchase second-hand phones, often saving them from the dump. He slowly built up his inventory so that a shortage could be avoided.

Once in awhile the New England line crews would leave the Bryant Pond company a windfall, dropping off bunches of used wire being replaced with newer cable, and he was able to get sturdy older power poles from Central Maine Power Company when they periodically upgraded their electric lines.

One time New England ran a toll cable from Bryant Pond to Rumford. The route went right by the Hathaways' telephone office.

"I think I'll see if the cable crew would bury a new one for us at the same time," Elden told Barbara. "The old lines we have in now are getting worn. Every time we have a rain, they short out."

She agreed with him, and they scraped together enough money to buy new cable which New England was happy to install.

Occasionally a vacationing telephone man would volunteer to work on the Bryant Pond lines "just to recall the feel of how things used to be".

Chapter 16

HOW DOES IT WORK?

When Barbara and Elden bought the company, they had three toll circuits connecting them with the outside world. Every call placed outside the limits of the subscriber resulted in a toll ticket written out by hand and timed by the switchboard operator. The cost of the call was determined by the Public Utilities Commission. When they acquired the system, the record for long distance calls was 29 in one day. This total was reached when someone became lost on a nearby mountain, and the rescuers had to call for volunteer searchers from surrounding towns. That record was broken the first New Year's Day that the Hathaways owned the company.

It wasn't as easy to get a call into Bryant Pond as it was to call out. Many city operators had never heard of a ring-down operation, and callers were often frustrated by being told that they weren't providing enough numbers.

"I can't dial that for you. There must be more digits. Are you sure you have the whole thing?"

Once a caller from the outside world learned the correct route, the operator was usually enthusiastic about completing the call. It made her feel like a pioneer.

Whenever Mike called from Boston, and even Susan from Australia, they would tell the operator, "Your route is 207+093+121. That will give you Norway, Maine. From there you ask for the Bryant Pond operator and tell them you want line 32." Line 32 was Barbara and Elden's personal phone number. Usually, the call went right through.

One of the first things the summer residents did when they arrived for the season was to see if their phone still worked.

"Oh, hello," would come a somewhat surprised voice. "I guess the phone got through the winter. How is everyone in Bryant Pond?" They would greet the operator like an old friend, filling them in on the latest news and glad to be back to the peace and quiet of Maine.

Of course Elden had already made a point of seeing that the summer lines were operational before the visitors arrived. A working line meant getting them off on the right foot for their visits.

As the world changed, new residents who moved into town were often appalled with the old phone equipment. They watched in amazement when it was installed in their homes.

"I don't see any dial on the phone. How do I make this thing work?" they worried.

Elden patiently explained. "In magneto phones, the crank is connected to a small generator that sends a current along the wire until it gets to the office. There it knocks down a drop on the switchboard and the operator will then stick in a plug and answer your call. You need to keep the receiver on the hook when you ring or else there won't be enough power to knock the drop down. Now, to know if the call is for you, you will have to listen for the right ring. A number like 2-11 means you are on line number two, and the right ring for you to answer is a long ring followed by a short one. A number such as 8-32 indicates three long rings followed by two short ones."

Many of the visitors to Bryant Pond stayed for only two or three weeks. Even though they were not happy at first with the primitive utility, by the time their stays had ended, they too had learned to depend on the company as much as the year-round residents.

A busy summer's day at the switchboard included questions like,

"Where can I buy bottled gas? I think we're all out."

Chapter 16 - HOW DOES IT WORK?
Photograph by Jack Quinn, Lewiston Daily Sun, 1973

"Elden ... made a point of seeing that the summer lines were operational before the visitors arrived." Pictured : Jim Keen checking cable.

"What time are the local church services, and where can we find a Catholic mass?"

"Can you tell me what's playing at the drive-in in Norway or Rumford this week?"

"How long do I have to cook string beans before they are done?"

"My clock has stopped. Can you tell me what time it is?"

"Barbara, I'm going to be out of town this afternoon. If anyone calls, can you tell them I'll be home about 6:30 p.m.?"

"Oh, Bob, I'm going to spend the day at my sister's, and I'm expecting an important call. Would you be kind enough to transfer it over to her house?"

"Hi! We're staying at the Anderson Cottage for the next week. Can you help find a babysitter for a couple of evenings?"

- - - - - - - - - -

The Hathaways developed close ties with a family from New Jersey, the Powers. Their children Joyce and Hugh were close to the same ages as Mike and Susan. They first rented Rupert Hathaway's cottage on Lake Christopher. After a few summers, they built their own cottage at the foot of the lake. The end of the summer always seemed a little sad, and the Hathaways hosted a traditional farewell breakfast before the Powers returned to their winter home.

Gertrude Powers was a trained nurse. One day when she was visiting Barbara at the switchboard, a call came in from an anxious mother vacationing in Bryant Pond.

"Please help me!" she cried in a panic-stricken voice. "My child has just swallowed a penny. I don't know what to do. What can I do?" she asked over and over.

Barbara turned to Gertrude. "The best thing is to get the child to a doctor," she advised.

"But I don't have a car!"

"Don't worry," Barbara reassured her. "I have a friend here with me who is a nurse. We'll be right down to get you and take you and your daughter to the hospital."

She called the nearest doctor, some twenty miles away, to tell him that they were bringing down a child who had swallowed a penny. "I'll meet you at the hospital," he said. Fortunately Bob was at home, and he quickly arrived to cover the switchboard. The women picked up mother and daughter and drove them to the hospital.

After the little girl was examined, the doctor said, "She is in no danger. I'm going to give her a good dose of caster oil. The penny should work its way out."

"Thank you so much," the young mother said to Barbara and Gertrude as they returned to Bryant Pond. "I don't know what I would have done without you."

Chapter 17

LIFE LINE TO THE COMMUNITY

For many of the elderly citizens of Bryant Pond, the telephone company was their life line to the world beyond their homes. Knowing that help and companionship was just a crank of the phone away brought them comfort and a feeling of security. The operators knew who needed to be checked on and monitored their existence daily.

Susan took a call one day from an old man. "I can't make any sense out of what he's saying," she told Linda. "I think he's all mixed up. Keeps talking about his wife." The girls decided to locate his daughter in Bethel and told her of their concern.

"I'll be right down," she told Susan.

They later found out that the old man's wife had fallen and broken her hip. Because of his senility, all he knew enough to do was turn the crank to try to get help, but his words just wouldn't come out right.

Another elderly gentleman who lived alone sounded concerned one Sunday as he came to the telephone office to pay his bill.

"Say, if anything should happen to me while I was at home," he asked, "and I was able to turn that crank, would you answer?"

"Sure, that's all it takes," Elden reassured him. "We'd know who it was."

Within the week, Barbara was tending the board when the old man's drop came down. She could barely make out his voice.

"Help me," he pleaded. "I've just been robbed and beaten."

A thief had entered his house and stolen his Social Security money, assaulting him in the process. Although he was badly hurt, he was able to crawl to the phone and call for assistance. Barbara quickly notified the police and the rescue squad.

Burglar alarms were few and far between in Bryant Pond. Most people even left their doors unlocked. The Coles purchased one for their small grocery store in North Woodstock which was connected to their home close by in case of an after hours robbery. They had a phone installed which did not make a ringing sound when cranked so that they could silently notify the switchboard operator to get the police.

One of the town's more prominent citizens, General Alger, traveled a great deal. Before going away, he would rig up a wire through the inside of his house which was connected into the telephone line. When it was disturbed, a battery wired to the line would send a constant surge of power to the telephone switchboard, making it impossible for the operator to keep the drop up. That was the signal to call the police.

The most dreaded words for an operator were, "There is an emergency. We need help."

From car accidents to heart attacks to fires, the reaction of the person tending the switchboard could make the difference between life and death, between saving a home, or losing one.

- - - - - - - - - - -

"Please help! Call the police! My husband is beating me!" a woman pleaded to Barbara one evening. The next thing she heard was a crash, and as the phone dangled off the hook, Barbara helplessly listened to the woman's screams as the fight continued. She called the Sheriff's Department.

One weekend almost all the firemen were out of town when a call for help came in. Andrea desperately searched about town, but was only able to locate a couple of volunteers to go to the blaze.

Those were the hard times when the operators did everything humanly possible to help and then had to let fate take its course.

One year Bob got a fire department call the morning of Town Meeting. He couldn't get hold of a single fireman, and there was no phone at the high school gym where the citizens had gathered. Wracking his brain for a solution, he called Cleo Billings who lived near the school. She was at home.

He asked her, "Would you please go right over to the meeting and tell Harold Tyler there is a fire!"

The hall soon emptied as the volunteers sped off to the blaze, and town business came to a halt until they returned.

Cleo had to come to the aid of the phone company one other evening when another fire was called in and all the volunteers were at a fire department fund raising dance in the gym.

By the 1980's the town had its own rescue squad, and the fire fighters all had plectrons and radios for early notification relayed from the Sheriff's Department in South Paris, but the operators were still the ones they called when they needed fast guidance to a disaster scene.

UPS drivers made their daily stops at the Hathaways for directions, and so did the occasional salesman. When the National Guard was holding maneuvers up on the Gore, they would stop in at all sorts of odd hours to call their home base.

One delivery truck driver called from Cole's store looking for directions for a lady who had just let the operator know she was going to be at Irene Mills' for two or three hours.

"Do you know where the telephone office is?" Elden asked.

"Yes, I do," the driver declared.

"You should find her at the house right across the street."

The lady was surprised when her purchase was delivered to Irene's house.

"Do you know where my mother is?" a little girl asked Andrea. She had arrived home from school to a empty house.

"I think she's at the store. I'll see if I can get her there." "Hi, Ethel, your daughter is looking for you."

Debbie gave comfort to another young lady home alone during a thunder storm. She gave her advice on where to wait out the thunder and lightening, and then called after the rain had ended to make sure she was all right.

Whenever a drop came down on the switchboard, the operators knew that there was a chance they might need to deal with an emergency situation requiring a calm reaction, with speed and accuracy.

\- - - - - - - - - -

One summer evening, Elden was relaxing after a day's work on the railroad, enjoying a rare night of not being called out on a line, when a young woman driving a wreck of an old car and carrying a young baby, no more than a month old, knocked at the office door.

"I'm staying at my relatives' place on the back side of the lake, and someone in town suggested I should come here to find out about getting a phone put in."

"Gee, I'm sorry. I don't have a single one at the moment," Elden replied. It was a time when money was tight, and he could only afford to purchase a few at a time. He had just installed his last one.

The young woman looked like she was going to cry.

"You can't be alone over there without a phone. I'll find something for you," he continued, scratching his head for an answer. "I just put an extension in for a friend up the street. Maybe he'll loan it to you until I can get a replacement. Give me Bud Jenkins," he asked the operator.

"Hi, Elden. What are you up to tonight?" Bud asked as he recognized his friend's voice.

"Bud, I've got a big favor to ask. Can I borrow your phone?"

"What?"

"We've got this young woman over here with a little baby who is staying on the back side of the lake. I'm fresh out of phones, and they shouldn't be living there without one. I didn't know but you might loan me back the extension I just put in for you until I get a replacement."

"Sure thing - be glad to," Bud agreed.

Elden went down the street and removed the telephone. Then he headed for the old place where the young woman was staying. The entrance road to the cottage had been used sparingly and the last few hundred feet were impassable except by foot. He went to work

Chapter 17 - LIFE LINE TO THE COMMUNITY
Photograph by Bill Haynes

"Whenever a drop came on the switchboard, the operators knew that there was a chance of an emergency." Pictured L to R: Althea Hathaway, Genneth Berryment, 1979.

stringing wire through the trees and fastening the protector box on the outside of the house. By the time he got inside to hook up the phone, the woman had found that the water pump wouldn't work, and she was also out of gas for the stove.

"As soon as I get this installed, I'll tell you who to call to get things working," Elden comforted her. She was able to reach the help she needed that very evening.

"Thank you so much," she said as he headed home. "I don't know what we'd have done without you."

Chapter 18

OPERATOR ASSISTANCE

Bryant Pond telephone operators always went out of their way to complete calls for their customers. Sometimes it meant continuous attempts to reach an out-of-town party while the customer went about his business, knowing he would be called when the operator was successful. Occasionally, a much harder assignment would materialize.

"Elden, we've had a family emergency and have to get hold of my brother and his wife who are on a guided tour somewhere in France." The lady was upset and turned to him for help.

"Do you know where abouts they are?" he asked.

"I have an itinerary of where they were going."

"Let's see what we can do," he said. He got as much information about the trip from the lady as he could, and put a call through to the place where he thought they might be.

"They've already been here and left," he was informed by the French operator who was assisting him.

The second call, however, was successful, and the woman was

able to talk to her brother and inform him of developments at home.

- - - - - - - - - -

"Elden, we've just got home from Rhode Island, and we're kicking ourselves that we didn't buy an item we found in an antique shop. We just have to get it! The problem is we forgot what town it was in, but it was located right next to this dog kennel."

They described it to him, down to the smallest detail.

Elden called an information operator in Rhode Island and explained what he was trying to do.

"Oh," the Rhode Island operator said to him as he described the dog kennel. "I know where that place is." She went on to tell him the name of the antique shop and its telephone number, and within a matter of minutes the Bryant Pond customers had located their treasure.

- - - - - - - - -

Although operators did not make a habit of listening in on calls, a lot of customers took it for granted that they did. In the later years of the company, it was almost impossible to do even if one had wanted to because they were so busy.

Althea Hathaway, who joined the company in 1967 became so fast at tending the board that she could carry on a conversation with someone and at the same time complete other calls. Lots of times all one would hear her say would be "-perat'r" or "thank y--"

A social call with Althea during a busy stretch on the board would sound like:

"Oh, hi, Ann, what's new today. -perat'r thank y-- -perat'r thank y-- -perat'r thank y-- Oh, you don't say, Ann. -perat-r thank y--."

There were, of course, a couple of customers who were never pleased with any of their efforts, and the girls would fight (good-naturedly) over who would not have to answer their calls.

"I don't think you girls are ringing the right number. They should be answering."

"What took you so long? I turned the crank three times?"

"Can't you do anything right?"

"We're sorry," they always apologized, even though it was rarely their fault.

- - - - - - - - - -

The operators had to be very tactful as well as helpful, and have a good memory.

"I'm going to take a nap," Mrs. Smith informed the girls on the switchboard. "Please don't ring my phone until after four."

"Sure thing," Andrea agreed. The elderly lady was in the habit of making this request.

A few minutes later a long distance call came in for her.

"I'm sorry, we can't ring that number until after four," Andrea said.

"Well, this is her son, and I want you to put the call through."

"She instructed us that no one was to disturb her."

"Look, don't you understand! This is her son! Now please ring her phone."

"Is this an emergency?"

"No, I just want to talk to her."

"I'll be happy to tell her you called, or you can try back again when it's time."

"Damn you, operator, I want you to ring the phone now!"

"I'll tell her you tried to reach her. That's the best I can do."

Slam went the receiver in Andrea's ear. "Sometimes it's hard to be diplomatic," she sighed as she went about the rest of her work.

- - - - - - - - -

"Susan, we're having a wedding at our house, and we'd like to have you hold the calls while the service is going on."

- - - - - - - - - -

"Linda, my husband has a headache. Can you ring the bells softer?"

"I'll only ring once, and then make it a short one," she smiled.

- - - - - - - - - -

"Bob, how do you spell hospice?"

"H O S P I C E"

"Oh, thanks," the lady on the other end laughed. "You're the only person in town who could have spelled it."

- - - - - - - - - -

One day an elderly lady placed a call through Linda to a doctor's office. After a couple of minutes, Linda checked to see if they had finished their conversation. She heard a loud highpitched "eeee" sound when she opened the key.

"Oh my gosh," she said. "I've never heard anything like that before. Something must be the matter with the line." And she pulled the plug.

She described the sound to Genneth who was working beside her.

"Oh no," she said, "the lady has a pacemaker, and she was giving the doctor a reading over the phone!"

Linda quickly recalled the old lady and the doctor, apologized and explained what she had done. They had to start the procedure all over again.

- - - - - - - - - -

"Hello, operator, this is Betty Johnson. My phone bill for last month was out of sight. My kids have got friends in Bethel, and they talk for hours at a time. I'd like to put a stop to their toll calls."

"We can put a note up on the board not to take any out-of-town calls from your number," the operator suggested.

"Oh, that would be great." Mrs. Johnson sounded relieved.

She worked until 5 p.m., and most of the calls were made in the afternoon when she wasn't home.

"The directions for the other operators will be posted right in front of your number, and no out of town calls will be made without your OK."

The next day her son placed his usual call.

"I'm sorry," the operator on the board informed him. "We have instructions not to place any out-of-town calls for this number."

"What do you mean!"

"Your mother requested that the number of toll calls be cut down."

"Oh, she doesn't mind if I call Bethel. She'll approve."

"I'm afraid I can't put it through for you."

"You just wait! I'm going to get you in trouble with the Hathaways!" Slam went the receiver.

Sometimes parents would put a quota on the number of calls their children could make each day. It didn't take long, however, for the kids to figure out when the operators changed shifts.

"I think you've made the number of calls you're allowed already today," the night operator would say.

"Oh no," answered a youth innocently. "This is my first one, honest. I still have two more after this one."

If the switchboard was busy, there wasn't time to go back and check the toll tickets.

- - - - - - - - - -

During the summer months the Conservation School located on the back side of Lake Christopher would play host to teenagers from throughout the state. With each new session came the usual scramble to call home and let everyone know they'd arrived safely. Few of the youths had ever worked a hand crank phone before.

"Ring..."

Down would go the Conservation School drop.

“Ring..."

"You can stop turning the crank now."

"Ring..."

"Hello!" the operator would yell. "You only have to ring once."

"Oh - teehee - this is Bullford P. Moose, III. I'd like to call

855-5555 collect, please - teehee..."

There was usually so much noise in the background that the person on the board could hardly hear the call.

"Bullford P. Moose, III?" she exclaimed. "Those kids use the craziest names."

"Ring..."

The operator answered and her ear burned from power on the line.

"You can stop turning the crank now..." she yelled. Another kid was on the line.

- - - - - - - - - -

Whenever an animal strayed away from its owner, someone in town usually notified the telephone operator, thinking they might know who the owner was.

"Debbie, do you know whose big German shepherd has been hanging about the center of town? He looks like he might be lost."

"Barbara, there are some ducks wandering around the street over on the Patch. I'm afraid they're going to get run over. Do you know where they belong?"

"Bob, this is an emergency! My pig is loose and running down Route 26! Please get me some help!"

Althea was working the board one day when the Gore Road line drop came down.

"Several cows just went by my house," the caller said breathlessly, sounding worried. "They were right in the middle of the road, and no one was with them. Have you heard of anyone looking for them?"

"Gee, they might be Bob Day's," Althea replied. "I'll give him a call."

She rang his phone several times, but there was no answer. Thinking quickly, she went down the list of subscribers living on the Gore, hoping to find a few who could help round up the cattle until the owner was located.

"Hi, this is Althea at the telephone office. There are several head of cattle loose near you, and we aren't sure whose they are. Would you be willing to help round them up?"

"Ayah," the man on the line responded.

She was able to find a few helpers who happened to be home and were willing to give it a try. She knew from the first caller which way they were headed, and as they continued on their trek, other subscribers called in, telling Althea of their sightings.

With up-to-the-minute information on their location provided by the phone company, volunteers organized for the roundup and headed the cattle into a nearby vacant fenced-in pasture. There they safely munched on green grass until their owner was able to take them back to his farm.

Genneth Berryment was tending the switchboard when she was notified that her pigs were loose. Without blinking an eye she directed their recapture, right from the phone company office.

In times such as this, when help was needed, neighbors could always be counted on to lend a helping hand, and more often than not, the telephone operator was on the line coordinating the whole effort.

Chapter 19

GIVE ME THE FRENCHMAN ON THE CORNER

"Oh, darn. Jerry Farrar's at it again," Bob would sigh.

The old man lived alone in a large old house at the foot of Merryfield Hill, just across from the beginning of Rumford Avenue. Lame and crippled from years of hard work as a carpenter, he walked bent over, hitching along, dragging one foot behind him. He was also very deaf.

"Hello! Hello! Hello! Would you speak up please. I can't hear you." Jerry's telephone was on a party line, and he couldn't tell his own ring.

"Jerry, the call's not for you. Would you hang up so I can get the right party."

"Hello? Hello? What'd you say?"

"I said - hang up! The call's not for you!" Bob would yell as loud as he could. "It's no use," he said as he explained the problem to the caller.

"I'll try it again in a couple of minutes. Maybe he'll move out of range of the phone."

This routine became more and more frequent as the old man's hearing deteriorated. Other attempts usually got the same results.

"Hello? I can't hear you."

Shortly afterwards Farrar's line drop came down.

"Operator," Bob greeted the call.

"Are you calling me? Speak up, will you?"

"No, Jerry, we don't want you."

"The situation is getting drastic," Bob finally told Elden. "We've got to do something about Jerry Farrar. He doesn't know when a call is for him, and if he hears the phone ring at all, he picks it up. I haven't been able to get a call through on that line all day."

"Well, I guess there's no choice but to give him a private line. That way when he does hear the ring, he will know it's for him."

Elden made the change and explained to the old gentleman that some of his long-time friends would be on a different line.

As his hearing got worse, his speaking voice got louder. When his drop came down, the operators developed a special technique to answer his calls. Whoever was on the board would remove their headset and shout "Operator" into the mouthpiece. Then they would hold the headset at arms' length while Jerry roared.

"Give me the Frenchman on the corner." He had never used a phone book in his entire life, didn't know any numbers, and couldn't remember the complete names of some of his friends. It wouldn't do any good to try and change him now. Eventually he was confined to his bed and needed a nurse to care for him, but he kept his hearty voice til the end.

Barbara, Elden, and all the operators took a special interest in all their older customers. Another one would give the operator the number he wanted rung, then show his impatience by clicking his false teeth and saying "waiting, waiting, waiting" until he got an answer from the other end of the line.

Chapter 20

KEEPING THINGS LIVELY

As Linda grew older she developed a sense of humor and spent hours thinking of ways to play jokes on her older sister. With Mike away at college, she enlisted the aid of the operators.

"Bob, will you help me?" she pleaded. "Mother just made Susan a new sheath dress for her concert at Gould Academy, and I think it's a little tight. I want to play a little trick on her when she comes in to show it off. Will you drop something on the floor and ask her to pick it up? I'm going to hide in the folks' bedroom, and when she bends over, I'm going to rip an old sheet. I can't wait to see her face!"

Linda took her place and patiently waited.

Susan made her entrance.

Bob called her to the switchboard.

"I dropped my pencil on the floor," Bob said with a sense of urgency. "Will you pick it up for me?"

Susan bent over.

R-R-I-P...

With a look of horror, Susan stood up abruptly and checked the material covering her behind.

Linda convulsed into gales of laughter.

"I don't think you're funny at all!" Susan scowled and stalked out of the room.

Linda was also always there to entertain Susan's boyfriends when they called. She was not above giving the young men insights into how her sister felt about them. She maintained a profitable business by being so inquisitive that she was paid to leave the room - not only by Susan, but often by her company as well.

Linda also delighted in scaring poor Bob. She was constantly leaping out from behind doors and yelling "Boo!".

Even with eight years difference in their ages, the girls would compete fiercely to win at card games such as Pounce. The loser usually would wind up throwing her cards on the floor in disgust.

Linda did not share Susan's interest in the board. She had no desire to learn how to tend it. In high school, however, she successfully applied for a job as a telephone operator at Norway's toll center. With the skill she learned during those summers, she found herself also being pressed into service when needed at home. In college she came home most weekends to earn $1.50 an hour for tending the switchboard.

- - - - - - - - - -

"Linda, what's the matter?" Elden asked one night, soon after she started tending the board. He had noticed tears streaming down her face as she tried to work.

"Oh, I guess I'm not doing a very good job. A man just told me I was the worst operator he had ever heard, and informed me I shouldn't be working. I'm sorry."

"Did you goof up?" he asked.

"I don't think so. He was mad 'cause I didn't get the number right the first time he said it."

"Do you know who it was?'

"Yes."

"I think I'm going over and have a little chat with him!"

Elden drove to his house and met the disgruntled customer face to face.

"I understand you don't like how my daughter handled your calls."

"What do you mean?" he asked.

"Whatever you said to her made her cry. She's a very conscientious girl, and is trying real hard. Now, if you don't like it, we'll take your phone out right now!" Elden looked even bigger when he was mad.

"I'm sorry. I didn't realize. It's been a hard day," he apologized.

Elden accepted the apology and returned home. The customer was always a polite and patient caller from that time on.

- - - - - - - - - -

In 1965 Bryant Pond celebrated its sesquicentennial anniversary, the 150th year since the town was chartered. Many special festivities were planned, and everyone looked forward to them with much anticipation. There would be historic exhibits, a town supper, a field day at the ballfield, and of course a parade.

There was also a beard growing contest for the men of town. Elden decided to enter. He had became so attached to the beard that after he had shaved it off, he wanted to grow one again. This time it was there to stay, and his gray beard and crewcut hair became his trademark.

The telephone company decided to enter a float in the big parade. Elden got the use of a logging truck, and the family entitled their float "We don't use Dial". One of the props was a large box of soap designed by Bob McKeen. It carried the slogan "100% pure". The family band performed on the back of the truck beside telephone lines and an operator tending a switchboard.

The parade traveled through town to the ballfield where the

judging took place. They won third prize.

- - - - - - - - - -

Althea had a touch of bursitis in her shoulder one summer which gave her trouble reaching the drops to answer calls. Barbara found her a step stool which allowed her to work at a better height. When she wasn't working, the step stool was folded up and kept on a shelf next to the window near the switchboard.

One evening Debbie and Carol were working, and no one else was at home. Barbara and Elden were staying at their cottage on the lake. Carol was tending the position nearest the window. Debbie's board was quite busy, so Carol leaned over to answer one of Debbie's calls. As she reached to the side, she accidentally hit Althea's stool.

"Oh no!" she gasped as the girls watched the step stool crash right out through the window.

"What was that!" a customer asked when she heard the sound of breaking glass. "Are you all right over there?"

"I'm not sure. I just knocked a stool clean out through the window," Carol answered. "What number did you want anyway?"

Debbie looked at Carol. "Oh my gosh," she said, "how are we going to explain this?"

"Maybe we hadn't ought to disturb them at camp," she reasoned. "Let's call one of the telephone repairmen."

They explained to him what had happened, and he good naturedly agreed to come over and clean up the glass and put some plastic over the opening.

"Remind me not to upset you girls," he laughed as he lugged the stool in from outside. "I can see how violent you get.

"I'll put in a new pane in the morning. Barbara and Elden will never know the difference."

And the girls all conveniently forgot to tell them about the accident.

- - - - - - - - - -

Linda discovered an X-rated recorded phone message service the summer she worked in Norway. When she had a few dull moments at her position, she would dial the number and call a friend or the Bryant Pond operator on duty. With just the right timing she could connect her unsuspecting "friends" to the start of the X-rated message when they answered the phone.

"Hello," began a low sexy voice. "I'm so glad you called..." The one-sided conversation continued from there while Linda listened for her friend's reaction.

- - - - - - - - - -

April Fool jokes sometimes took a good deal of planning.

"What do you say? Let's get Andrea!" Debbie said to Eleanor as April 1st drew near.

"You know she's been on this diet binge where she has to eat yogurt every day, and she never eats the same flavor twice."

The girls found a flavor she hadn't tried, apple spice, and promised to bring her one to sample. Before she arrived, they went into Barbara's kitchen and added some oregano, garlic salt, and a few other edibles, being careful not to change the color or texture.

"Isn't this great. We're going to have a yogurt party," Debbie said as all three prepared to eat their lunch together.

Andrea took one taste and bolted to the bathroom. Debbie and Eleanor contorted with concealed laughter as they listened to her gargling with mouthwash to get rid of the awful taste.

"I think something's wrong with that yogurt," she said as she came back to the office. The girls couldn't hold it in any longer, and they all had a good laugh.

- - - - - - - - - -

One Halloween the girls decided to get the telephone repair-man. Debbie and Andrea spread peanut butter on the steering wheel, put bags of wet macaroni on the driver's seat, filled his vehicle with balloons and put confetti behind the visor.

"He'll be getting in after dark. It should give him a real start!"

Not only did they get him that night, but the next day when the sun shone in his eyes, he pulled the visor down and got a face full of confetti.

- - - - - - - - - -

Three of the repairmen's wives happened to be pregnant at the same time, so the girls decided to give the boys a baby shower, complete with cake and icecream. The embarrassed workers opened boxes of pampers and baby clothes while the operators looked on with glee.

- - - - - - - - - -

On slow days one shift would design scavenger hunts for the next shift, leaving clues throughout the house, with a box of candy at the end of the trail as a reward. The last clues read something like, "You have finally reached your destination" or "The end".

- - - - - - - - - -

The family of telephone workers stuck together, one picking up the slack when another had a problem or was just plain down in the dumps. Debbie, the teenager, had ten "mothers" who constantly worried about her, and she responded to their caring by bringing them all carnations on Mother's Day.

Chapter 21

THE BAND

A few years before the Hathaways bought the telephone Company, Elden's elderly aunt, Fanny Whitman Ross, came to live with the family. She had grown up in Woodstock but spent her married and then widowed years in the Rumford area. She had come from a musical family. Her brother Bertrand was considered a child prodigy, studying at the Boston Conservatory of Music at the age of 16. He had made his living as a professional musician, and when he was semi-retired in the 1950's, summered at the Whitman homestead on the old stage road between Bryant Pond and West Paris, until it burned.

Aunt Fanny played the piano and violin until she had to stop when cataracts clouded her vision. At her encouragement, the family purchased a piano, and Mike and Susan started lessons. The Professor used to give a recital at the end of each summer, combining local children and his musician friends from Massachusetts. Mike and Susan had to spend long hours practicing while the short old man stroked his waxed mustache and gritted his teeth as he tried to make them into musical virtuosos.

One year he decided to give Mike an old cornet and provided him with a few lessons to get started. Mike practiced on the front porch, and at first he sounded like a sick calf as the sound bounced off the ledges across the road. At the same time Mike's two cousins Dean and Jim Bennett began to learn the banjo and trombone. Dean's wife started the accordion, and Charlie McAllister found an old tenor saxophone. They got together and tried to make some music but had a lot of trouble keeping the same beat.

"You guys can't keep the rhythm," Elden observed after listening to their futile attempts. "I think I know where I can get a set of drums. I think you'll play better with someone keeping the beat." He had always wanted to learn. He banged on a lot of pots and pans when he was young, and now he had the perfect excuse.

The set he brought home had been stored in a chicken coop for many years. He paid $20 for them.

The going was tough at first. Sunday practice sessions lasted a couple of hours, but they slowly learned to play together. The group practiced in the Hathaways' dining room in front of the house so that the telephone operator could hear the calls coming in on the switchboard. The old animal hide drum heads would sound "punky" on rainy afternoons.

"I think we're ready to perform," Dean announced after a half year of the weekly practices. They had mastered five songs.

"Let's play at the weekly record hop down at the high school gym. I've got to chaperone next week anyways," Elden suggested.

They did so well that they came back later in the evening to play the same five songs over again.

Mike and Jim went on to major in music, and both became band directors. Susan became an accomplished organist, and Linda, while trailing behind in age, also received a degree in music. Her instrument was the oboe. Elden continued to play drums for many local dances and took a great deal of pride in the family band.

As the years passed, the family members continued to play together. Dean's second wife played the piano, his children Cheryl and Rick learned the clarinet and trombone. Mike's kids, Brian and Brenda, played bass, tuba, piano and French horn, and both earned music degrees from the University of New Hampshire. Jim's children, Leslie and Jason, learned oboe and drums. Linda's children, Sarah and Rachel, took up flute, violin and piano.

- - - - - - - - - -

When Mike started the cornet, the telephone operators soon found another use for his talent.

"Mike, get your horn out please. We have a receiver off the hook."

Chapter 21 - THE BAND
Photograph by Hathaway

"They got together and tried to make some music but had a lot of trouble keeping the same beat." The original band is pictured here in 1957: (L to R) Mike, Charlie, Elden, Dean, Luna, Jim.

In the old crank systems, there was no dial tone, and when a phone was accidentally left off the hook, a ground on the line was created and the bells would not ring. If the customer was close enough to the receiver, he could hear any sound made on the other end. Mike would grab his old cornet and blow as hard as he could into a telephone transmitter. Anyone near the open receiver would hear the noise.

"Hello? Oh, I'm sorry. I must have left the phone off the hook. What was that strange sound anyway?"

Mike would pack his horn away and wait for the next request.

Chapter 22

THUNDERSTORM

It usually occurred on a hot and humid summer's afternoon. The crackle and snaps of the static on the long rural lines would be the first warning for the telephone operators. The storm's direction most often followed the string of lakes north of Bryant Pond down to the Little Androscoggin River whose headwaters flow south from Lake Christopher.

Whoever was on the board would pass on a warning to the members of the Hathaway household who were home at the time. Barbara would hurry outside to take her wash off the line and close windows in the cars and house. The kids would stop what they were doing in anticipation of the coming storm's fireworks display.

Its strength was measured by the increasing intensity of the static on the line. The air would grow still, not a breeze flowing, and the humidity was almost unbearable. The sky turned light and then very dark.

"Snap!" A spark flashed from the switchboard as several drops came down at once. Even though it was expected, the operator jumped. Carefully the drops were pushed back with the eraser end of a pencil so as not to get a shock.

"I think it's time to move back away from the board," the operator cautioned.

Thunderstorms always produced a show of fireworks at the telephone office. Each wire that came into the building was a potential lightning rod. Whenever a strike hit near a telephone line the electric charge would be transmitted over the wires all the way to the office.

Each house with a phone had a fuse box on the outside wall. The fuses were about 5" long and looked like pencils. They had a thin wire inside that was designed to melt when a strong electric charge was sent through it. Many of the fuse boxes were also connected to ground rods providing an outlet for the lightning. When the wire in the fuse melted, it usually stopped the charge from doing damage to the phone and other parts of the house.

Most customers knew enough to avoid using the phone in a thunderstorm unless it was an emergency. The Norway toll center, however, carried on business as usual. When Bob McKeen answered them, he would hold onto the plug by the cord trying not to touch metal.

"I'm sorry, but they may not answer. We have a thunderstorm going on," he often had to tell the toll operator.

In heavier storms balls of fire often leaped off the switchboard.

"That does it!" yelled Bob. "I'm getting back to a safer distance. You kids had better go to the bedroom!"

Everyone got away from the board.

"Buzz" Norway kept on ringing.

"Crack" and "Boom"!

By now everyone was in the bedroom peeking out to watch the action when they dared.

As the storm subsided, Bob would return to the board and

report on the damage.

"Look at this," he called back. "Almost every drop on the board has been knocked down."

"Operator - yes, we're back in business."

"I wonder how many phones are going to be out of order," Barbara worried.

"I'll start calling the customers," Bob volunteered. As he did so, he prepared a list of those who couldn't be reached. This was given to Elden to tackle when he got home from his day job on the railroad.

One particular storm did a lot of damage.

"You're not going to like this," Bob told Elden. "It looks as if about a third of our customers are out of order. I've got Basil Green and Mike ready to go."

"Let me get a bite to eat, and then I guess we'll have to work until dark. Would you make a list of those who should have their phones fixed first? You know, anyone sick or old or who can provide necessary services."

The fuses were the first to be checked. Usually a phone outage after a thunderstorm meant a fuse had been blown. A quick check with the ohmmeter told the story. If no current passed through, the fuse was replaced. Then Mike would knock at the door of the house and ask the occupants to call the office. If no one was at home, Elden would check from the fuse box on the Army field phone.

"Look at this!" Basil exclaimed one day as he followed a line back to a cottage on the shore of Lake Christopher. "Here's a place where there's no wire at all. The electricity must have burned it up."

"Well, look here," called Mike. "This piece of line has the insulation but no wire inside. Wow, is that strange! It even blew the fuse box all apart!"

"There's no way we can fix all of this tonight. I guess I'm going to have to take the day off from the railroad tomorrow to finish the job," Elden sighed. "Let's head for home. It's nearly ten."

He and Mike visited John Hemmingway's in Pinhook the next day.

"Gosh," John said, "that lightning came right in and blew the phone right off my wall - never seen such a thing!"

"Well, it's a goner," Elden said, looking at the phone. "We'll have to replace it."

Finally by mid-afternoon everything was pretty much returned to working order. Back at the office an all-too-familiar crackle could be heard over the lines - another storm was approaching!

Chapter 23

CHARLIE, QUIT FOOLING WITH THE LIGHT

Eventually the old milk wagon had to go. The family needed a vehicle that was more efficient and comfortable for traveling, and at the same time the telephone company needed something to carry its equipment.

"Let's face it," Elden said. "The old rig is on its last legs. The kids are growing, and now that I'm coaching the Little League ball team, I need something we can carry the players in." He and Barbara finally agreed on a 1950 Ford station wagon that doubled as a telephone "truck" during the day and a family wagon, ball team transporter and Eastern Star bus at night. Within a year or so afterwards a chance for a real bargain popped up.

"The Bell phone system has traded some of its phone trucks, and I can buy an old one in South Portland for only $250."

"Do you think we can afford it?" Barbara asked.

"Well, think of all the wear and tear that the station-wagon gets. I think it's a good deal," he reasoned.

They decided to buy it, and she took him to South Portland to drive it home. However, he got off to a rocky start. The old truck stalled several times in heavy city traffic, and he wasn't sure if he ever would get it home.

It eventually proved to be a good truck even though it had a habit of getting stuck in low gear. Once Elden had to drive it ten miles at a snail's pace before he was able to reach Tyler's Garage. On winter mornings when the temperature would drop to as much as forty below the truck would be the only vehicle in the yard that would start. Elden would have all the other cars lined up in a position to get a jump-start from the truck's battery.

When Mike went to Boston to college, Elden quickly found out that it was not easy to hold a flashlight in his teeth while fixing troubles, especially up a pole at night. Mike used to help aiming the spotlight from the old truck while his dad found and fixed the broken lines.

"Charlie, would you be willing to go out with me and hold the light while I work on lines at night?" Elden asked the McAllister boy one Sunday afternoon as they watched the football game in the switchboard office. It was a regular weekend ritual.

"Sure, I'd be glad to," the young man replied. He began to accompany Elden on his night excursions.

One spring evening he called for Charlie's assistance.

"We got trouble down by the parsonage. I'll pick you up in ten minutes."

"OK, Elden, I'll be ready."

The pastor's residence was located next to the Baptist Church. There was a steep bank on the opposite side of the street from the church property that led downward to a swampy area. Three quarters

Chapter 23 - CHARLIE, QUIT FOOLING WITH THE LIGHT
Photograph by Hathaway

"It eventually proved to be a good truck... On winter mornings it would be the only vehicle...that would start."

of all the wire that serviced the telephone customers was hitched to the poles on the street by the parsonage, making it hard to find an individual line. A canvas saddle tied them into one big clump.

Elden parked the truck in a location where Charlie could focus the spotlight on the work he was doing up the pole. He set up his ladder, climbed the pole and went to work.

"OK, Charlie, move the light just a little to the left. Now up just a bit - that's fine. Oh, by the way, could you find and toss me up a roll of tape. I forgot to bring any with me."

Charlie rummaged around in the back of the truck and brought Elden his tape. Then he stood by to watch him complete his work.

"Hey! Quit fooling around with that light," Elden complained. "I can't see what I'm doing."

"I'm not fooling with any light," Charlie yelled back.

"But it's moving," Elden protested.

They both looked towards the truck which was beginning to slowly roll down the hill.

"There goes the truck!" Elden shouted. He watched helplessly as Charlie ran after it. By then it had gained speed, rolling down around a curve, right across the road toward the steep bank, the boggy meadow, and the brook.

Charlie got close enough to get his hand on the door just before it left the road.

"Let her go!" yelled Elden. Charlie jumped clear, and down the bank it went.

"That will be the end of the truck," Elden told himself as it disappeared down the embankment.

He hurried down the pole with a sick feeling in his stomach, and together he and Charlie went to inspect the damage. Miracle of miracles, the truck remained upright and seemed to be in pretty good shape.

They walked home.

"Harold, would you be willing to pull my truck out tomorrow with your wrecker?" Elden asked the garage owner a little while after he had caught his breath.

Elden had to work on the railroad the next day, but afterwards he went to the garage to see what was left of the truck.

"Well, I guess you can drive it home," Harold told him. Not a bit of damage was done." Not even a tool was lost!

Chapter 24

TIME TO EXPAND

The old Western Electric switchboard had been with the company for years, and by 1960 every space for an incoming line was already connected up. There was no room for expansion. The board had also become very temperamental, and once in a while, it would decide to take a "rest", leaving the operators holding their breaths until it started to work again.

"Clarence Todd has an old Kellogg board that's bigger than ours. It was used by Oxford County Telephone Company in Turner, and he'll give us a good price," Elden told Barbara. "We really need to have more line space. I even think I can get him to wire it up."

They moved the "new" one into the office, placing it behind the old one. Clarence wired them together. When the job was finished, the old Western Electric was cut free. Service wasn't even interrupted. The "new" one was never quite satisfactory, and the Hathaways had to replace it again in the late '60s.

In 1970 a young man from New Jersey came to Andover to visit his grandmother. His grandfather had been a telephone executive, and since his childhood days, he had been fascinated with phones. He had even hooked up a neighborhood line with all his young friends. While driving through Bryant Pond, he stopped at the local store and noticed the crank pay phone outside. He called up the company.

"I just had to try this out. I'm such a fan of magneto phones!" He identified himself as Tom Thurston, and after a few minutes of conversation, Elden said, "Why don't you come on over for a visit?"

He spent a couple of hours with the Hathaways and even answered a few calls on the switchboard. He returned for two more visits during his stay in Andover, and then took a trip to England where he wrote Bob McKeen about how much he had enjoyed the town and the telephone company.

The workload at the company had become almost unbearable, and Bob McKeen was now not only answering the board and doing the books, but was also helping supervise the line repairs.

"We need to do something about getting another helper who knows something about telephones," Bob said.

"I agree," Elden responded. "I wish I knew someone we could get."

"Well, I think I do. You remember Tom Thurston? He wrote me and said how he would really enjoy working for the company. The only problem is that he's on vacation in England."

"Do you know where he's staying?"

"Yes, I do."

"Let's call and see if he's interested."

He was. Elden picked him up at the Portland airport just before the 4th of July 1971. He stayed at the Hathaways until he found a place

Chapter 24 - TIME TO EXPAND
Photograph by Hathaway

"They moved the 'new' one into the office...The 'new' one was never quite satisfactory."

to rent. There was plenty of room in their home as Susan was in Australia teaching school, Linda was in college, and Mike was teaching school in New Hampshire.

Tom learned quickly, and Greenwood's Rowe Hill newspaper correspondent, Sandra Martin Dunham, praised him in the paper. "ROSE AWARD...to Tom, Tom, the telephone man...fixed the wires and away he ran. Never have I seen such dexterity in a pair of hands as his nimble ten fingers disconnected one set of bells, now making it necessary for us to have someone sit constantly by the phone, just in case it might ring. The changing of the guard, however, is most colorful. Actually, Tom deserves the ROSE...it works like a charm. Now, someone call and we shall see if it works."

During the winter months the topic of conversation centered around the increasing demand for private lines. It would not be long before a second switchboard would have to be added.

"I have a small Kellogg at home in New Jersey that I think could be hooked up beside the one in the office," Tom suggested. Since Linda is planning to fly to Australia to visit Susan after school gets out, I could take her to New York to get the plane, and bring the board back with me," he suggested.

"Great idea!" Barbara and Elden agreed.

It took a while to complete adjustments on the smaller unit to make the two compatible, but on May 30th, 1977, the Bryant Pond Telephone Company expanded to two switchboards. This solution was just temporary, however, and in January of the following year, a larger 140 line Stromberg-Carlson replaced Tom's smaller one.

During the busy morning hours two operators could now take care of the heavy volume of calling traffic. It took a little practice to learn to stay out of each other's way. Cords would intertwine, and at times the switchboards looked like a weaver's loom.

In 1974 the Hathaways learned that Norway was planning to eliminate their toll center.

Chapter 24 - TIME TO EXPAND
Photograph by Jack Quinn, Lewiston Daily Sun, 1973

"The workload had become unbearable...Tom learned quickly."
Pictured L to R: Bob McKeen, Tom Thurston.

"How do you suggest we get calls in and out when you close?" Elden asked New England.

"We suggest that you become your own toll center." That means you will have to have switchboards that accept and send dial calls."

After a couple of years of planning, New England Telephone Company set a date at the end of May 1977 to terminate the Norway toll center.

"I think I know where you can get a pair of switchboards in good condition up in Nova Scotia," Andy Hinckley told Elden. He had recently toured the island. "They're changing over to dial up there at a rapid rate."

Elden found two North Electric magneto switchboards for sale for $1200, and he took his van over on the Bluenose Ferry from Bar Harbor to pick them up. Engineer Art Fisher added dial blanks and wired the two new ones to the older pair. For a time the office was crowded with all four boards taking up a lot of space in the middle of the floor.

On June 2,1977, the older boards were cut free, and the operators plugged into the Bryant Pond toll center. By the end of the day the girls had mastered the new dial toll call system. Local callers saw little difference in the service, but out-of-town callers could now dial the company direct rather than place a call with their area toll operator. It was much faster. The North Electric switchboards were the last ones the company bought, and they stayed in service until the cutover to dial six years later.

Chapter 24 - TIME TO EXPAND
Photograph by Hathaway

"For a time the office was crowded with all four boards taking up a lot of space in the middle of the floor."

Chapter 25

THE GREAT PHONE BOOTH

Howard MacKillop's grocery store had an old oak phone booth which served callers well during the day, but it was not available after hours. There were no other public phones available at night for travelers going through Bryant Pond.

"Is it OK if we move it outside?" Elden asked Howard. "That way there will be a phone for people to call from after the store closes." Howard agreed.

The booth was heavy, and it took several men to get it out onto the porch of the store. However, the old booth was not designed for the elements, and within a year the glue in its joints broke. It became very rickety.

"It's time to build a new one," Elden decided, and he went to the lumber yard and bought some pine paneling. He hammered and nailed until he had created a beautiful wooden structure with a glass in the door. This booth was designed to keep the wind and the rain out. He was especially pleased with the way the outside looked.

"It looks so good I think I'll panel the inside too!" he concluded.

Next he made a corner stool to sit on, complete with a balsam fir cushion to give it a fresh clean smell. He varnished it inside and out until it gleamed. It was very rugged and heavier than the old one, and the crew labored to move it into position in front of MacKillop's store. The old rickety booth was hauled away to the dump.

One of the first callers was a large man vacationing in town. He called the operator.

"I want you to know what a beautiful phone booth you have here. It's the first one I've ever been comfortable in, and it smells so nice. In fact, I'm so impressed that I've forgotten who I was going to call!"

Chapter 25 - THE GREAT PHONE BOOTH
Photograph by Hathaway

"He hammered and nailed until he had created a beautiful wooden structure with a glass in the door." Pictured here with Howard MacKillop.

Bob typed up a set of instructions to help travelers not familiar with a hand crank telephone:

"Do not deposit money until you get the operator.
"Crank the phone before picking up the receiver.
"Pick up the receiver and wait for the operator.
"Do not deposit money until the party is reached."

A quarter made a deep bong. A dime made two dings, and a nickel was a light bang. A local call was five cents. Out of town rates varied.

"Would you deposit thirty-five cents for the first three minutes, please."

Bong. Ding. Ding.

"Thank you. You may talk to your party now."

If the customer deposited the wrong coin, the operator could tell by the sound and ask for the right amount. Sometimes the caller would talk overtime, and once in a great while they might try to sneak away without paying the extra charge. If the store was open, the operator would call and ask the clerk to go outside to remind the offender that he or she still owed money. They usually paid up.

Occasionally a Canadian traveler who spoke only French would call from the pay phone.

"I'm sorry, I can't understand you," Bob would try to explain. "One moment please." Then he would call Rita Abbott who spoke fluent French. "Help," he'd say. "I have another French customer on the line."

"Hook me up," Rita would laugh, and she would proceed to translate.

About two weeks after the new phone booth was in operation, someone used it as an outhouse. Its abuse continued, and once it was even tipped over and the phone stolen off its wall. The phone was found a couple of months later in a drainage ditch with the cover holding the coins pried off.

When MacKillop's store closed, Elden had it moved around the corner of Main Street to in front of the Village Store. By now it showed signs of wear. There were countless initials carved in the soft pine wood. The glass was gone, and the once gleaming varnish was covered with paint. The vandalism continued, and Elden contemplated taking it out of service, but it was still the only source for public phone calls at night. It was especially needed by truckers who drove their rigs through town at all hours. Elden gave up keeping the window and door on it. He just turned it away from the north wind to help make the caller as comfortable as possible.

By the time the company went dial, there were five pay phones in service, but the pine phone booth was the only one outdoors.

Chapter 26

I'M SORRY WE DON'T HAVE A LISTING FOR THAT

Most all small rural phone company employees had a special camaraderie with the customers that their big sister city companies did not. The operators were always willing to help and assist callers in any way they could. For a while, however, there was one exception - the Bethel Telephone Company. Its owner decreed that his operators were not to engage in frivolous conversation with their customers or fellow operators AND they were not to give out numbers if the caller did not ask for the "proper listing".

There happened to be a very popular eating spot in that town known to the locals as Martha's Restaurant. Martha was the owner. A Bryant Pond telephone customer called one evening wanting to make a reservation for dinner.

"Can you ring me Martha's Restaurant in Bethel," he requested. Elden called Bethel and asked the girl on the switchboard to connect the caller.

"I'm sorry, we have nothing listed for that name."

"You know," Elden returned, "the place just before you get to the railroad tracks as you head south of town."

"I'm sorry, I can't help you."

"We'll have to go through the telephone book til we find it," Elden told his customer. Name by name he checked the Bethel listings.

"Here it is under Roadside Grill." He gave the right number to the operator in Bethel, and the call was completed.

A couple of days later a Buckfield operator called the Bryant Pond switchboard.

"Can you help me get the number of the restaurant in Bethel by the tracks? The operators won't help me at all up there."

Bob McKeen was happy to help Buckfield locate the telephone number.

Elden also had the same problem locating an insurance salesman in West Bethel. Fortunately he was able to get the number from another Bethel customer with the same last name whom he called by mistake.

"Bob, two can play this game," Elden finally said. "The next time Bethel wants any help, give them exactly whom they ask for." They didn't have to wait long.

"Can you give me the Whitman that does the plumbing?" It was Bethel calling.

"We have several in the book," answered Bob. "Which one would you like?" He knew full well which one it was.

The Bethel operators had to guess which one, and it took them several tries to find the right Whitman.

Another request. "Can you give us the Dudley Farm?"

"We have several Dudley's listed."

They chose old Carl Dudley by mistake who could just barely talk on the phone.

The phone information war was on.

In the meantime, Martha found out her customers were having trouble calling her, and when the owner of the Bethel Telephone Company came in for pie and coffee as he usually did each morning, she confronted him.

"What do you mean by not giving out the number of my restaurant!"

"Well," the owner replied, "you charged me for that piece of pie, didn't you?"

"You're darn right I did!"

"If I had another, would you charge me for that, too?"

"You're darn right."

"Well, you're listed as the Roadside Grill. If you want a listing under 'Martha's', it will cost more money," he reasoned.

"Why didn't you say so in the first place!" She gave the telephone company owner a check right then and there for several different listings.

A truce was finally reached, and the information wars cooled down again. The Bethel and Bryant Pond operators were pleased to reestablish a spirit of cooperation between the companies.

Chapter 26 - I'M SORRY WE DON'T HAVE A LISTING FOR THAT
Photograph by Jack Quinn

"We have several in the book...Which one would you like?"

Chapter 27

SNOWSTORMS

During the1950's any type of wet weather usually spelled trouble for the telephone company. Moisture would cause the old Army field lines to become grounded. Snow created more problems, especially when it was wet enough to cling to the wires. The extra weight would often result in a break. There was also the possibility of a tree limb coming down and breaking the wire. Little by little, Elden and his crew were able to improve and upgrade the older lines with cable and rural C wire. The open iron wire that often tangled was replaced first.

Heavy snow could do a number on the open wire, and Elden would have to take his pick pole and walk along under the line until he unsnarled the mess. The next wet snow, he'd be right back again.

"My phone is awful noisy, and I can hardly hear you," the customers would complain.

"We can't hear you very well, either," the operator responded. "I'll ask Elden to check it out as soon as it stops snowing."

Once the weight of the snow made a line sag until it was buried in a snow bank. Elden called from the house and found it was working.

"I'll just hitch it back up the pole," he said.

When he dug it free, he muttered to himself, "Well, I'll be darned. It's broken." Somehow the customer was able to talk from his house over the broken wire. The snowbank must have acted as a conductor carrying his voice to the other end of the break and on to the telephone office.

The winter of 1969 was a particularly bad one, highlighted with a four foot snow fall in one four-day storm. The community and the phone company were just about paralyzed. Elden pressed as many repair workers as he could find into service. The roads were so clogged that it was nearly impossible to get to the places needing repair. The repairmen used snowshoes or wallowed up to their middles. They worked without letup until the phones were in operation once more.

"Do we have school today?" The calls started in early after a storm.

"No, you don't."

"Oh boy!"

Sometimes the answer was, "Yes, you do."

"Oh darn!" came the reply on the other end of the line.

The school department called the Norway and Rumford radio stations, but many families could not hear the signal or wait until the announcement was on the air. The telephone company was the place to call.

From five o'clock on, during or after a storm, the calling would be as heavy as in the middle of a usual morning.

"Can you put me through to the mill? My car's stuck, and I can't get to work."

"Can you call Harold at the garage to see if he can pull me out of the bank?"

"My gosh, the phone still works! Can you ring my daughter? I want to see how she's feeling."

Once a heavy wet snowstorm weighed down several telephone lines where they crossed the main highway. A fully loaded logging truck came through and pulled them all down. Elden and the crew were soon back at work in the cold snowy weather.

Chapter 28

OVERLOADED

It roared down Rumford Avenue past the telephone office belching heavy diesel smoke as it headed west. The payload of lumber it carried was well over the legal height limit prescribed by state law. Tree limbs were left swaying in its wake, leaves and branches strewn everywhere. The trucker knew he was over the limit, and he hoped no one would be able to get a description or license plate number as he sped past.

"Did you see that?" Barbara asked an operator as she heard the truck roar by, catching only a glimpse of it out of the corner of her eye. "I'll bet he'll tear half the lines down between here and Pinhook. I'd better let Elden know so he can take a ride out there to check for damage."

He and Mike set out in the truck, finding and fixing a few broken wires as they followed the trail down the highway.

"Look!" shouted Mike as they drove along Whales Back. "There's some wire in the road!"

Elden stopped the truck.

"It looks like the new rural C line we just put up out in Milton Plantation, but that's a couple miles away. You don't think it got dragged all the way over here?"

Sure enough. The downed line led towards Milton. When they reached the other end of it, Elden pulled over and stopped.

"We only have that one stretch of rural C up, and the length of this seems to be about right." Elden scratched his head. "I guess the only thing to do is hook onto it with the truck and pull it back to where it was pulled down."

That's exactly what they did, hauling the wire several miles until they got to the place where it was supposed to be.

"Yup!" exclaimed Mike. "There's no line on the pole where it's supposed to cross the road."

Elden continued to drive until he reached the other end. The "rural C" wire was so strong that it did not break when it was yanked off the half mile length of poles by the logging truck.

It had been secured and held tight by a device called a "clip" The clip was crimped onto the rural C by a pair of lineman's pliers. The wire was held on to the pole by hooking its loop over an open-ended U-shaped threaded bolt called a drive hook. The bolt was hammered and twisted into the wood pole. Wherever a line was spliced, crossed the road, or went to a house, the wire was held by two "P" clamps that created a loop of slack wire at the pole. The "P" clamp was made of two sections that fitted over and under the line, holding it fast by friction, with the larger section having a wire loop attachment that slid over the drive hook.

Elden inspected the line as he reattached it to the proper poles. "You know," he pondered, "the only thing wrong is that the insulation has been skinned where it was held with the clips. I can repair that with tape. This wire is really something! If it will hold up a against a truck, it should withstand most any natural element."

From then on, whenever the telephone company could afford to, Elden systematically replaced the old Army surplus wire with rural C, starting in the remotest areas. The investment saved a lot of money and time in repairs.

Chapter 29

BASIL GREEN

During the memorable winter of 1969, Elden had to hunt for additional helpers to repair the lines that broke under the weight of the heavy snow. One such recruit was Basil Green, a local character who earned his living working in one or another of the wood mills in the region. Basil liked to live life to the limit. He was a drummer and ran his own dance band. Basil worked out to be a good telephone repairman most of the time, willing to tackle jobs that many of the crew would not try. He proved himself that winter, and Elden approached him in the spring.

"Basil, I will be needing some help from time to time on line work. You've been a big help this winter. I don't like going out alone at night anymore. I could bust my neck, and noone would find me for hours. Are you interested in giving me a hand now and then?"

"I sure would, Oz! I can always use the money."

Basil's nickname for Elden was "Oz".

Most of the time the pair worked well together. Basil, however, was not a man for detail. He often would leap before he looked. More than once Elden had to come to his rescue when a poorly placed ladder would slip around a telephone pole.

One time Elden came around a corner of a house just in time to see Basil literally running down the ladder as it slid out from under the pole. He kept his feet moving til he hit the ground.

"Are you all right?" Elden shouted, fulling expecting him to have a couple of broken legs.

"Yes, I'm fine," Basil answered as he bounced back to his feet. "I kept moving so I wouldn't land so hard!"

"Well, if you keep that up, I'm going to get you a cape so you can fly like Superman!" Elden chuckled, relieved that he was all right.

Another time Basil was working on the tree at the office right next to the Hathaways' new station wagon. Elden got a sinking feeling as the ladder went flying again, and he watched it and Basil headed straight towards the vehicle. Basil landed next to the rear tire, his feet sliding under the car.

"I'm going to have to get you collision insurance," Elden said, shaking his head.

On a cold, windy, sub-zero night just before Christmas, the pair went out to fix a trouble on the phone line that ran down by the public wharf. The wharf was a cement and stone outcropping on Lake Christopher built for boaters and swimmers. Elden located the problem in a group of large fir trees close to the lake. He decided that the easiest solution for repair was to run some new wire and splice it into the old, thus eliminating the bad section. After one end had been connected, Basil went up the pole on his ladder to make the final splice.

The wind was blowing a gale, and he just couldn't get those seven little wires into the copper sleeve.

"You know, Oz, if I only had a drink I think I could get my fingers working!"

It so happened that Elden had bought a fifth of brandy just that afternoon for the family's Christmas eggnog, and it was still in the vehicle.

"If you come down here a minute, I think I can fix you up with a little warmth."

Down Basil came, and the two huddled in the cab taking sips of the holiday brandy.

"Ah, now I think I can do it." Up the ladder he went again.

He still couldn't make the connection, and after a few more minutes he hollered down, "Oz, I got to have one more sip. My hands are still too cold."

Back to the truck they went. The two men shared another drink.

"All right, let's get this over with." Up he went again.

Still no luck. Back and forth Basil climbed until the fifth was nearly gone.

"OK, Oz. This time I know I can do it!" By now Basil was having trouble climbing, and he swayed back and forth on the ladder as the wind blew. The pain in his hands, however, had subsided enough so that he was finally able to make the splice and restore service to the lakeside customers. Elden went to the liquor store the next day and replaced the fifth of Christmas brandy.

It was not unusual for a telephone wire to carry a small amount of electric current. The current often resulted from a phone line being too close to a power source, or a faulty power company transformer. One time when Elden was going to splice a line back together, he got an especially large jolt of electricity.

"Here, Basil," he said. "Why don't you connect these two while I start picking up the tools?"

Basil obliged and took his boss's place. He grabbed hold of both sides of the bare wire and got a shock that almost knocked him over.

"Damn! I just got a hell of a jolt!"

"You don't get power on a phone line," Elden responded, trying to keep a straight face. "Someone would have to be turning the crank on their phone."

He tried again, and dropped the line.

"Well, it sure looks like someone's got my number!"

Basil was always very affable, and the prospect of a good drink and some conversation sometimes made him forget about the work he was supposed to do. One spring weekend the pair was checking out the summer resident phone lines in back of North Pond.

"Basil, why don't you follow the line down to the cottages and see if everything's OK. I'm going to meet you right back here."

"OK, Oz," he said, and off he went.

The task should have taken only a few minutes. After an hour or so, Elden muttered to himself, "Where in tarnation is he! Maybe he's in trouble."

He set out following the wire, finding no sign of Basil. Before long he saw smoke coming from the chimney of a cottage.

"Well, I bet that's were he is!" he said to himself. And there he was, sitting on the porch, having a beer with the camp's owner. He'd totally forgotten all about meeting Elden.

Chapter 30

THE BULLDOGS

One day someone made a request that changed their lifestyle for several years. "Elden, my folks recently died, and they had three bulldogs. We've sold two, but the third one, a three-year old female named Beauty, seems to be very lame. We didn't feel right about selling her and had just about decided to have her put to sleep when someone suggested we contact you. I understand that you are fond of bulldogs and might be willing to give this one a try."

"Well," Elden thought, "It's been a while since I've had a dog, but I sure would like to give this one a chance."

"OK, we'll bring her up," the caller said with relief.

When the dog arrived, she took an instant liking to Barbara and Elden, greeting them with her short tail wagging. Then she spied the cat, and off like a shot they went, round back of the house and by the telephone office window.

"She doesn't seem very lame to me," Elden chuckled.

Althea was on the switchboard. "What was that!" she hollered out the door.

"Oh, that's our new bulldog!"

They brought her into the office to show Althea. "And what's her name?"

"Beauty."

"Beauty?! You've got to be kidding. I don't see anything beautiful about her. She looks like she hit a wall going seventy miles an hour," she laughed.

And so the newest member of the family was introduced to the switchboard. The dog lost any symptoms of lameness, and Elden speculated that the cement floor of the barn where she had been kenneled might have caused her condition.

"What do you say, let's have her bred," he suggested to Barbara. She agreed. The first litter produced three puppies, and they kept one for themselves, named Winger.

The animals became part of the standard photo session, posing for the press and TV crews who continued to come to Bryant Pond. The dogs added to their nostalgia stories. Elden was often photographed supervising the line repairs with a bulldog on a leash, and when he did an interview, one of them would likely be sitting on his lap.

Winger was named by Australian friends of Susan. They were visiting at the time the pup was born. Winger loved to chew, and one of her toys was a rubber ball with a bell. Little by little he worked a hole through it, spurred on by tinkling inside.

Finally, one evening he succeeded in making the hole large enough to get at the bell. Suddenly Winger ran whimpering into the telephone office.

"My gosh!" the operator said. "He's got something stuck to his tongue." She called Elden at the cottage. "You'd better come over here right away."

He took Winger to the vet who got the ball off the end of the dog's tongue. "You'll have to keep ice on the tongue tonight so it won't swell."

"Susan, since you're tending the switchboard, would you feed him some ice every time you get a call?" Elden asked.

"He's going to keep me up anyway," she sighed.

Winger was a very curious animal. One day he decided to visit a young lady riding her horse. By the time Elden found him, he was bouncing around under the hooves.

"He's going to get trampled," Elden worried as he hurried to rescue his pet. "Come here, you!" he called as he reached for the dog's collar and pulled him to safety.

Winger also had a passion for fresh vegetables, and one year ate the only eggplant Barbara had ever been able to grow. If Elden forgot and left him alone in the van with a supply of freshly picked produce, the dog would enjoy sampling a portion of each variety.

Beauty was the one, however, who commanded the greatest attention from photographers because she was the ugliest, a typical bulldog. She slept in the bathroom.

When Debbie Farrington joined the company she did not realize this, and on her first night alone she had to visit the facilities. Between calls she raced through the kitchen into the bathroom, closed the door and reached for the light. Suddenly her hand froze in the darkness. She could hear heavy breathing.

"Oh no!" she thought. "Someone's in here with me!"

Mustering all her courage, she bravely said, "Oh excuse me," praying it was one of the family. At the sound of her voice, Beauty snorted and rolled over. It took Debbie the rest of the evening to stop

Chapter 30 - THE BULLDOGS
Photograph by Hathaway

"During the 70's, the Bryant Pond Telephone Company was clearly dominated by the bulldogs."

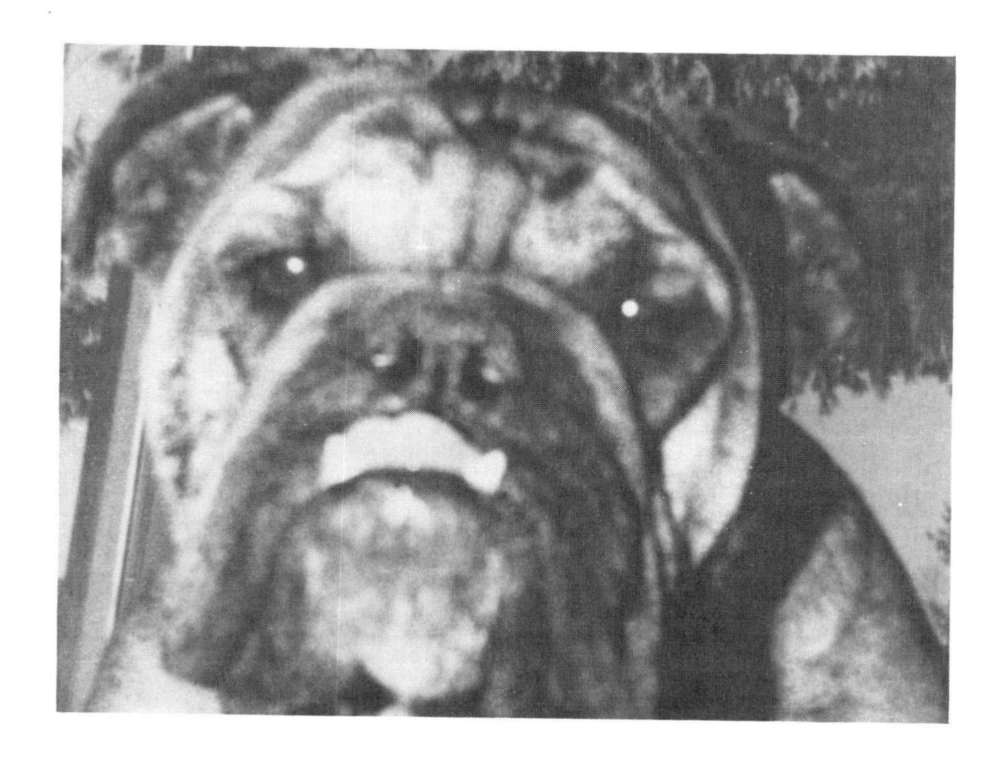

shaking.

During the '70s, the Bryant Pond Telephone Company was clearly dominated by the bulldogs.

Chapter 31

NIGHT OPERATOR

"I think it's time we hired one of the girls to work nights," Elden suggested. "Wouldn't it be nice to stay right at the cottage for the summer."

Elden really loved his place at the end of the lake. From its breezy front porch he spent hours in his easy chair, listening to the Red Sox play baseball and looking out over the water. He had designed the cottage himself and had been involved in almost every step of its construction. It became a place of refuge, especially during the month of August when he was on vacation from the railroad. He hated to drive the five miles home at night to tend the switchboard.

Back from Australia and without a teaching job, Susan agreed to operate the board five nights a week from 9 p.m.to 8 a.m. Barbara came back to the house to cover the other two nights. Usually Sue was able to get to sleep before midnight, and the first call of the morning would be around 5 a.m. By 8 a.m. when her shift was up, business had picked up enough to need two operators. She slept on a sofa bed in the office and was guarded by the family bulldog Winger. He made his bed next to hers and was not happy when the night alarm sounded. She had to crawl over him to get to the board.

"Get away!" Sue would yell at the dog as he nipped at her ankles. "Winger let go!"

Even after getting past Winger, she would find the other bulldog waiting at the switchboard who expected some attention too! Fortunately for Susan, at least one of the dogs usually stayed with her folks at camp. The times they were both together, Barbara would come to the rescue.

- - - - - - - - - -

Three a.m.

The alarm goes off. Susan struggles to get away from the dogs and staggers to the switchboard. It's an incoming out-of-town call.

"Bryant Pond? Is that really you? This is Jim Midnight from WEIX in Seattle, Washington. We read about your old crank company, and thought we'd give you a call. It took us a while to find out how to get hold of you. You're now on live radio in Seattle, Washington. How does that feel!"

"Another radio station!" Susan muttered under her breath. Ever since the hearing, late night talk show hosts from all over the country tried to get through to Bryant Pond.

"I feel sleepy!" she said. "It's three a.m. here."

"Oh that's wonderful," the voice on the other end continued. Now would you tell our listeners what it's like to work for a hand crank phone company."

Susan pulled her robe around her and settled back for another middle of the night interview. Once in a while the host was considerate enough to call ahead for an appointment. National Geographic requested that they be able to come and photograph Susan at work on the board in her nightgown.

"Enough is enough!" she told her father. "I refuse to have my picture taken in my nightgown!"

- - - - - - - - - -

In May of 1978 Susan married Bruce Glines from West Paris. All the operators were invited to the wedding, but of course the phone company couldn't shut down, so a team of retired operators from

Norway volunteered to keep things running while the regulars joined the celebration. The newlyweds spent three or four nights a week at the office, Bruce sharing his bride with the callers and the bulldogs. Linda worked the remaining evenings.

"Dear, it's time to get up. It's 7:30 a.m. and the operators will be here in less than half an hour." Susan tried to move her husband out of bed. Come on, Bruce, if you're going to stay in the office, put your pants on. If you want to sleep some more, you're going to have to go upstairs." Bruce was working the late shift in the tannery in Norway. He didn't get in until 1 a.m. and was used to sleeping mornings, but he was forced to move upstairs to a bedroom with a little more privacy than the telephone office. While Bruce slept, Susan worked on the daily bookkeeping.

Chapter 32

EX-CON ENCOUNTER

"Excuse me, but this is private property," Elden said to a tough looking youth as he appeared to be making himself at home, parking his car on the Hathaway's camp road while having a beer or two.

"I don't see anything that says this is your land," the ruffian shot back.

"Well, it is, and you are trespassing. If you don't leave, I'll get the police and have you removed."

"Listen, old man, you'd better be careful. You might have an accident, or your cottage might burn down. If I were you, I wouldn't threaten me that way."

"Get out now!" Elden insisted, and slowly the intruder drove back out the camp road.

"This is not over yet," he said with a coy smile. "We will meet again."

Elden checked with the local cops in the hope of finding out more about this sullen young man.

"The guy just got out of jail, and he's a real tough cookie," one of his sheriff friends informed him. "You'd better be careful. He and his girl are headed for big trouble again - soon."

Barbara and Elden decided against staying at camp for a few nights until the problem blew over. Elden kept a pistol ready in case he came back. The next evening, now staying at home, they suddenly became aware of a car approaching the house at high speed.

"Do you think it's him?" she asked anxiously.

"I don't know, but if it is, I'm ready," Elden replied as he grabbed his weapon. The car swerved onto the lawn and made a loud crack as it mowed down their mailbox, fleeing on into the night.

"I don't know if they'll come back," Elden said as he called for law enforcement help.

"We'll check around," the sheriff said, "but he's probably long gone. If it is who you think it is, I'll take a run by his place tomorrow and see if I can find a dent on his car from the mailbox. I don't think you'll be bothered any more tonight."

Barbara and Elden found it hard to sleep as they waited for the safety of daylight.

The next day the sheriff did check the suspected car and found damage that looked like it could have been caused by running over a post or mail box.

Since being out of jail the young thug had caused quite a stir throughout the community, and reports of his bullish tactics began to surface. Each day the Hathaways hoped their cottage would be OK as they went there during the day and each night returned uneasily to their home, hoping the vendetta was over.

"Gee, this car just went by my place, and it must have been going well over a hundred miles an hour. Do you think I should call the police?" The call came in a week or so later from a customer on Route 26.

"I don't think I ever saw anybody go that fast! He's gonna have an accident and probably kill somebody." More calls came in with the same story, tracing the speeding car's route through the phone company's territory. The lines buzzed as neighbors called each other to compare stories.

"Who do you think it was?" everyone asked.

The answer came in the next day's paper.

"Young man and woman die in high speed crash. Estimated speed of the car was well over a hundred when it slammed into a tree killing the driver and his passenger. The vehicle is reported to have left a high speed trail through three towns before ending in death."

The driver was the young ex-convict who had terrorized the Hathaway household. With this bizarre ending, they could try to enjoy peace and quiet again.

Chapter 33

MERRY CHRISTMAS

"Hello," said a little voice on the end of the line. "I'd like to speak to Santa, please."

"Just a moment," the operator responded. "I'll see if I can connect you.

"Elden, we have another call for Santa Claus!"

"Ho! Ho! Ho!" boomed the husky voice as Elden picked up the phone. "This is Santa Claus. What is your name? - Have you been good this year? - What would you like for Christmas? - Merry Christmas! Merry Christmas!"

The happy child hung up the phone. It had become a Christmas tradition in Bryant Pond. The children there had a direct link to the North Pole.

Another young lady reeled off a long list of her wants, including a hi-fi set and a television.

Santa told her, "That sounds like a pretty big list, but maybe if you're good, you might get one of those things."

A few minutes later he got another call from the same girl. “Didn't I just talk to you?" he asked.

"Yes, but I'm calling for my father."

"What does he want for Christmas?"

"He wants a money making machine!" she said.

Once in the summertime a youngster heard Elden's laugh from the next aisle in the grocery store. "I know you," the young man shouted as he raced to get a look. "You're Santa Claus!"

Christmas time was always a special occasion at the telephone company. Bob McKeen had a flair for art, and each year he would design and make Christmas cards by hand for each of the customers.

"I don't know how you do it," Barbara would often marvel. "Each year your cards get better and better." He usually worked a month or more in between calls at the switchboard until his task was completed.

The office-living room was festively decorated with holiday trimmings and a small spruce tree cut from the power line where it crossed the bog. Many cards sent by friends, neighbors, and customers were hung along the walls. The operators were also remembered with

Chapter 33 - MERRY CHRISTMAS
Photograph by Glenn Richmond, 1972

"Ho! Ho! Ho! This is Santa Claus..."

Christmas goodies, and if that wasn't enough, the smell of Barbara's homemade breads and pastry and candy added a mouthwatering aroma throughout the house.

"Good morning, and Merry Christmas!" was the message for December 25th. The Hathaways greeted the town as it slowly came to life. When the children were all awake, they gathered around the switchboard to open their stockings and after breakfast had their presents, often interrupted while a call for the operator was answered.

During the early years of the telephone company, the whole family ate holiday dinners around the switchboard. As calling traffic increased, it was necessary to move the feasts to the dining room and leave whoever was tending the phone calls to grab a few bites whenever they could.

The Hathaways not only felt the warmth and love of their own home during the holidays, but that of almost every family in the community, sharing the excitement of the day with their customers as they called back and forth.

Chapter 34

BASIL GREEN'S CABLE MACHINE

"I think it's time we ran some cable over Church Street to connect with New England at the mill crossing," Elden told his crew. "I want to clean up that mess of single lines between there, the old West Paris Road, and Rowe Hill. The cable will also help us satisfy the demand for private lines."

People were using their phones a lot more, and even a four party line was as busy as an eight or sixteen line used to be. This was the first time the crew had taken on such a project by themselves. Elden had contracted previous big jobs out to cable specialists. His crew was used to handling smaller reels of wire such as the old Army field and rural C types, but the larger multi-use cable would require different equipment and handling.

"We're going to need a special hook-up on the back of the pickup in order to string the cable out. Do you boys think you can build something that will work?" Elden asked the boys.

They allowed as to how they could, and Elden left them alone as he tended to other matters, confident that they could figure out a solution. The telephone repair truck at that time was a snub-nosed pickup with the engine under the cab. Elden envisioned them building a cradle in the back of the truck's body and a ramp for rolling the big reel up into place. The crew had different ideas. One of them suggested constructing an apparatus modeled after the cable haulers used by the New England Telephone Company.

Basil Green thought, "Let's take some 2x6s and build a frame off the back of the truck. All we'll have to do is roll the reel up on a little ramp and slide an iron bar through the middle hole, and it'll be ready to go. All we'll have to do is pull out the cable."

They went to work and built what looked to be the perfect cable carrier. When Elden saw the finished product he almost went through the roof. It wasn't what he had expected.

"What the hell is that! Basil Green's Cable Machine?! That's the damnedest contraption I've ever seen! Don't you know that the pickup doesn't have any weight over the front wheels? You put that big reel on the back, and the front tires will come right off the ground!"

"Gee, Oz, we hadn't thought of that," Basil replied. "Since we have it all done, why don't we at least give it a try."

Elden gave in. "OK, but you know you have to haul the cable hooked up all the way from the office to Church Street."

The crew carefully maneuvered one of the big reels into place, rolling it up the ramp and sliding the iron bar through the hole in the center. The balance was so precarious that every time a worker jumped in the back of the truck, the front wheels went into the air.

"If you hit a bump," Elden warned, "you're going to be out of luck. You'll lose control of the truck."

"I've got another idea," Basil said as they got ready to leave the telephone company's yard. "I weigh over two hundred pounds. How 'bout if I ride up on the front bumper to keep the wheels on the ground!"

Elden drove another vehicle in front of the telephone truck with warning lights flashing. The procession slowly proceeded down Rumford Avenue with Basil clinging to the front of the pickup, providing the ballast for the cable on the back. Once the first few lengths of cable were pulled from the reel, the contraption did its job just as it was supposed to. Basil's weight was no longer needed, and he could climb down off the front of the truck.

Chapter 35

THE HEARING OF '73

Late in 1972 a family moved to South Woodstock, just inside the Bryant Pond Telephone Company's territory.

"I would like a private line," requested the new resident.

The Public Utilities Commission had established a somewhat complicated rate system for small telephone companies. Anyone living within a certain distance of the switchboard was entitled to a basic installation fee for service. Outside of that area, an additional charge for line construction could be made. The new resident was located two miles beyond the base area.

"I figure it will run about three hundred dollars to fix you up with a private line," Elden said.

"That's way too much money!" the new resident complained.

"I'm sorry but that's about what it's going to cost me to string the wire."

"Well, I can't afford that."

"You can have a party line for the basic rate. There's one that runs right by your place."

"A party line just won't do. I have to be able to get the line when I need it. I have a busy real estate business."

"That will cost three hundred more," Elden repeated.

The real estate broker was not happy.

Shortly afterwards Elden got a letter from the P.U.C. questioning the price he had quoted. The Commission felt it should be a lot lower. He tried for a couple of weeks to contact someone in their office so he could resolve the matter over the phone. When he did get through, it was obvious that someone had already been up to South Woodstock to look over the situation.

"After all, he does have a nice place, and he ought to be able to have a private line," the P.U.C. representative concluded.

"Then do you think it is within my right to ask for a deposit on the materials?"

"That is up to you."

"Then when I get one, we'll run the line."

After hearing his options, the customer decided to get the party line service. Strange noises, interrupted phone conversations, and unexplained troubles started happening to the line. It got so bad that Elden wouldn't let a repairman go out to the South Woodstock area alone. The real estate broker started complaining about the service to the P.U.C., and he even hired a lawyer to plead his case.

The board tried to work out a solution. They suggested to Elden, "Mr. Todd from the West Paris Telephone Company is willing to bring him dial service. His line is only a short distance away, and then the complainant would be off your hands."

"I'll bet he would," Elden returned. "In that case, would it be all right if I went into West Paris' territory to give service to some of the families who would rather be connected to Bryant Pond?"

"Oh no, we couldn't allow that," the P.U.C. said. "We have to respect the boundaries."

"There are a lot of companies throughout the state that have the same problem," Elden said, "neighbors having to place toll calls to neighbors."

The customer continued to complain.

"The only thing left to do is to have a hearing and determine if your service is indeed as poor as this customer says it is," the P.U.C. concluded.

"Good," Elden said. "Why don't we do just that."

Plans for the hearing were set in motion. A couple of Commission representatives unexpectedly stopped by the telephone company on a day when Elden was at work on the railroad, leaving Barbara to deal with them. Their message to her was most upsetting.

"It looks like you're in big trouble. It will be very hard to prove that you are giving good service with this old system. The best thing for you to do is hire a lawyer."

By now Bryant Pond was one of the last magneto systems left. It was a white elephant in the eyes of those who wanted modernization.

"Perhaps we should poll our customers and see how they really feel," Elden suggested. The company sent out 321 questionnaires with prepaid return post cards. 254 came back with the following results:

1. Do you think the magneto service in 1973 is satisfactory?
   Yes: 248 No: 6

2. Would you still be satisfied with this service with a moderate rate increase?

Yes: 237 No: 11

3. Would you prefer dial service with a rate between $8 and $12 a month?

Yes: 6 No: 233

Then the Hathaways hired a lawyer.

"You will need a questionnaire," he suggested.

"It's already done, Elden said.

"Good. Let's see if the results will work to our advantage."

"I don't think there's any question about that," Elden replied.

The hearing date was scheduled for 1 p.m. Thursday, August 9, 1973 at the Woodstock Elementary School gym. It was the hottest day of the summer. People started arriving early and soon filled the room to overflowing. There were not enough chairs for everyone to sit. The parking lot was full, and by the time the P.U.C. representatives arrived, they had to leave their cars way out on Route 26 and carry all their material and equipment a good quarter of a mile to the gym. U.P.I. and A.P. press reporters were there covering the struggle of the old ways versus the new. They followed the lead of the Portland Press Herald who had covered the events leading up to the big hearing.

The only parties to testify against the company were the complainant, his wife, and the owner of the local wood products mill who stated that it wasn't so much that he disliked the system, but that his customers had trouble completing their calls into Bryant Pond. As there were few "ring-down" systems left in the country, a great many operators did not know how to correctly place a call to Bryant Pond. Worse than that, often their supervisors couldn't find the correct routing either.

After the complainants testified, the moderator stated, "We'll now have a brief intermission, and anyone else who would like to testify this afternoon will be sworn in at that time."

Elden was called to the stand. He gave the results of the mail poll.

A great many loyal customers came forward to speak, including Harold Tyler, the fire chief. The rest of the day was spent listening to all the services and help the company and its operators had provided for their customers over the years. Some testified as to how the quick thinking tenders of the switchboards had actually helped save lives. Sterling Mills, the Hathaways' next-door-neighbor took the stand.

"Mr. Mills, what is your number?"

"Three - three."

"What is your profession?"

"I'm a logger."

"Are you happy with the service you get?"

"Yes, very much. Sometimes when I call a number, the line is busy, so the operator waits til it's free and calls me back with the other party. The only problem I have is that sometimes I forget who I was calling!"

"Do you have any trouble with your line?'

"If I did have any trouble getting them on the phone, all I would have to do is open my door and holler. Elden would be right round to fix the phone."

The hall roared with laughter. The temperature inside rose throughout the afternoon but hardly anyone left. At the end of the day Elden spoke again. It had been an emotionally draining ordeal.

"I would like to thank each and every one of you who came here today to listen and to testify - even the complainants for bringing this to

Chapter 35 - THE HEARING OF '73
Photograph by Jack Quinn, Lewiston Daily Sun, 1973

"We wish to express our sincere thanks to all the subscribers...and to those who wrote letters of support."

a head. I'd like to thank you for making us feel that the last twenty-two years haven't been for nothing."

The audience rose to its feet in a tribute to Elden and Barbara and the rest of the employees at the phone company. There were very few dry eyes in the gym. The P.U.C. stated that a decision would be handed down in about three weeks.

The August 16th issue of the Bethel Citizen carried the following card of thanks:

"We wish to express our sincere thanks to all the subscribers and interested people who were present at the public hearing on August 9. Special thanks to those who took time from their work and who traveled long distances to attend, and to those who wrote letters of support.

Elden and Barbara Hathaway, Bryant Pond Telephone Company"

Chapter 36

INTO THE LIMELIGHT

Papers throughout the country were filled with the accounts of how a tiny town in Maine had stood behind its old fashioned telephone company. The Portland Press Herald editorial on August 11 proclaimed, "Something Has to Go." The Telegram stated the next day, "Bryant Pond Residents Love Crank Phone Calls." And the Boston Globe ran a story August 16 headlined "What They Want Is Crank Calls".

Almost unnoticed with all the publicity about Bryant Pond, the only other magneto system left in New England, Meriden, New Hampshire, quietly switched to dial the weekend of August 25th, 1973.

The tension built as the town waited for the P.U.C. ruling. It didn't take long, and the results were carried nation-wide. The

September 9th issue of Washington Post quoted the Commission's decision in part. "We have carefully reviewed the complaint in this case and are convinced that the problem the complainants are having with incoming toll calls is not with the Bryant Pond system but rather with the unfamiliarity of Bell System personnel with the magneto system." The New York Times story stated, "Crank Phones Win Maine Reprieve."

The pressure on the Hathaways had been exacting. For the past six months Barbara had been bothered with eye problems. Medical checkups did not reveal anything seriously wrong. The couple spent as much time at their cottage as possible trying to avoid the constant pressure of the press. As summer came to a close Barbara's eye problems became more severe.

Elden was at the telephone office when word of the P.U.C. decision came. He was relieved and pleased with the results.

"Now maybe we can get on with telephone business," he told his wife by phone. The town celebrated the victory. "I'll be over to the cottage in a while, but I've got some stops to make first." He hung up.

Suddenly Barbara felt very strange and distant. "My eye-sight is going," she thought as she struggled to keep her senses about her. "I've got to stay calm. I must find Elden."

She rang the switchboard.

"Operator."

"This is Barbara. Something is the matter with me. Everything is just a blur. I can't see. Can you find Elden?"

"I think he's at Tyler's Garage. I'll try to get him."

"Harold, is Elden there?"

"Yes, he is. Would you like to speak to him?'

"Please."

"Hello, this is Elden."

"Can you come to camp right away? Something strange is happening to me," Barbara calmly said. "I can't see!"

"You stay put and relax. I'm on my way!" He was there in a matter of minutes.

He took her right down to Dr. Nangle in West Paris. By the time they arrived her sight had returned.

"I think you have an artery in your neck that may be partially plugged, and it's possible a small piece may have broken loose and entered your brain, causing a mini-stroke," Dr. Nangle stated. "I want you to go to a specialist in Lewiston."

An appointment was made the next day. After a series of tests, it was decided to operate on one side of her neck to clear the closed artery. Elden tried to keep Barbara away from the excitement of the hearing results and the press. They stayed at the cottage until she entered the hospital.

Chapter 37

HEART ATTACK

Barbara's operation was so successful that the doctors decided not to do the other side of her neck. The strain of the hearings, his wife's medical problem, and the pressure of the press slowly took its toll on Elden. He continued to work for the railroad, and he continued to weigh into the mid 200's.

"I don't feel just right," he told his wife one December evening in 1973 after a hard day's work. "I've got a very heavy feeling in my chest. I think I'll lie down."

The pain didn't go away. It pulsated down his arms.

"I'm going to call the doctor!" said Barbara. She was worried.

"Do you think you can take him to the emergency ward at the Norway Hospital?" the doctor asked.

"We'll leave right away."

"I feel foolish. It's probably just my hernia acting up," Elden told the doctor on duty as he was brought in.

He was admitted at once. Towards the middle of the night the pain worsened, and he was given a shot to ease the discomfort. Tests the next day revealed that he had had a heart attack.

"You need to lose weight and exercise," his doctor ordered, "and quit smoking." His recuperation went on schedule, and after a couple of months he was advised that he could return to work on the railroad.

"You mean I can swing a pick and shovel?" he asked the doctor.

"Oh no, you can't do any of that, or climb up and down stairs."

"That's all part of my job," Elden replied. "Will you put my restrictions in writing?"

"I will," he agreed.

Elden presented the doctor's orders to his boss on the track. "We'll put in for disability retirement," he said after reading the doctor's statement. "If Montreal approves, you won't have to work on the track again."

It was very hard on Elden to accept the fact that he would permanently need to change his lifestyle. At first he worked hard to remove weight and quit smoking. However, the resentment of having to change his lifestyle sometimes boiled over. He criticized the way his telephone crew did their work. He had always felt "if you want it done right, then you had better do it yourself". Now he had to let others tend to matters.

Barbara and Elden spent most of the next summer and fall at their cottage, letting Bob and the girls supervise the phone company business. Elden was usually available to do interviews with the press, radio and television reporters. There was now a constant flow of national interest in the Bryant Pond old crank company. The town was also growing, and demands for service increased. Even the peace of Lake Christopher did not lessen the pressure. It was not a relaxing or happy time for the couple. They wondered if they were losing hold of the fine service they had always prided themselves in giving.

Chapter 38

DOWN EAST MAGAZINE LEADS THE WAY

"I'd like to do an article on the Bryant Pond Telephone Company for Down East Magazine," Glenn Richards proposed to Barbara and Elden. He was a young writer living in town who had a keen interest in the last hand crank system in Maine.

"Well, if you think it's interesting enough for anyone to read about, go ahead," Elden replied.

Richards set about taking pictures and interviewing the Hathaways and the operators. The article appeared in the April 1972 issue. It was one of the first stories on the company to be read throughout the country. A few years later Down East even printed a picture of young Terry Cluky standing on a chair using the phone for a December 1979 Christmas gift subscription ad.

"It isn't that I'd planned to be the last hand crank company in Maine," Elden told his interviewer. "It would just cost too much to switch to dial, and I can't see going in debt for the next fifty years."

The Down East feature sparked a lot of interest from other news agencies. A Boston Globe article in December 1972 quotes Elden, "Yes, I've thought of going modern and having a dial system, but I think at least one magneto system should be preserved, so I guess we'll operate the way we always have."

It was interesting to see the company being discovered by the rest of the world.

"Elden, we have a call from ABC TV." The excited operator tracked him down.

"Hello," said the party on the other end. "I'm calling from 'Make a Wish', the children's TV show. We would like to come to Maine and film your telephone company for an upcoming segment."

"Sure, come ahead," Elden gave his OK. After a couple months planning a five man crew arrived to spend three days filming and gathering information. Back in New York the results were condensed into a five minute feature on the Saturday morning show.

The local correspondent to the Norway Advertiser-Democrat, Mrs. Sandra Martin Dunham, wrote the following article April 5, 1973.

"My beloved magneto phone line has come into its own. Oh, I get the works from the 'outer world', but Elden Hathaway gives his permission to tell these people who think we live in the dark ages this tidbit. That last description was my own, not Elden's. ABC-TV will be in town filming a 5-minute documentary for its program, 'Make a Wish', in May or June - its theme at the moment is things that are becoming extinct in America. Bryant Pond is only one of four or five crank service telephones left in the country. So - there you go. My hat's always off to that great switchboard downtown for just putting up with my calls."

The 'Make a Wish' segment did not air until November 4th, two months after the big P.U.C. hearing was reported throughout the country. The Bryant Pond Telephone Company was now famous.

WBZ TV from Boston came up in December, and NBC's 'Today Show' visited the town in January. An article in Yankee Magazine also appeared in the January 1974 issue.

In 1975 the American Telephone and Telegraph Company sponsored the making of a 30 minute film "To Communicate is the Beginning". The Bryant Pond company was included as the magneto link. Orson Wells did the narration.

The parade of the press eventually settled into a routine. Barbara would clean the house and wash windows ahead of time, bake homemade bread and prepare plenty of food to feed the camera crews. Elden would do most of the interviews. They all asked the same basic questions:

"What's it like to have all those crank calls?"

"What happens at night?"

"How does it work?"

"Can I call my home office from here?"

And they all wanted to see the same thing - a busy switchboard. If the lines weren't busy, the girls would fake it. Linda would go upstairs and ring the office. Barbara would call from the living room, and Elden from down in the cellar.

"Operator."

"It's just me. Are you busy?"

"No."

"OK, I'll ring again."

"Thank you for your call."

Most visitors accepted the company the way it was, but one

Chapter 38 - DOWN EAST MAGAZINE LEADS THE WAY
Photograph by Robin Moyer, 1982

"The parade of press eventually settled into a routine...Elden would do most of the interviews."

photographer insisted on rearranging the entire office. The interruptions eventually seemed worthwhile when the telephone family was able to see itself on a national TV program or pictured in a newspaper or magazine article.

Chapter 39

TERROR ON RUMFORD AVENUE

Not everyone who used the Bryant Pond phone system was polite and friendly. One such caller had been obnoxious all evening, demanding that he be connected to places such as the Pentagon and the White House. Like many of his age, active duty in the military had left him deeply troubled.

The operators were used to handling callers who might have tipped the bottle a little too much, but this call was different. It was the duty of the person on the board to ring the customer's request if at all possible. Elden was there to handle this particular party.

"I've got a guy on the phone trying to call Washington. He seems to be a little off in his head. I'm passing him on to you, and you can use your judgment as to whether you want to complete his calls or not," he told the Norway operator.

"I can pretend to ring the numbers he wants and then tell him there's no answer," the operator suggested.

He wanted the Pentagon.

"I'm sorry, there is no answer. They must be closed for the day," she said after a short wait.

"Give me the White House then!" he demanded.

After "several attempts" she said, "I'm sorry, sir, there is no answer there either."

"I know better than that. You S.O.B.'s aren't even trying to get my calls through."

He slammed the phone down.

"Maybe he's given up," Elden hoped.

The caller cranked the switchboard again, "I want Bob McKeen. He's the one that won't get the people I want. I've got a good mind to teach him a thing or two. He isn't fit to be alive!" he raged.

Elden pulled the plug and refused to answer any more of his rings. Finally his calls stopped.

"Maybe this time he's finished," Elden told himself hopefully.

Bob McKeen lived about a third of a mile down the avenue with his elderly parents. It was only a few minutes' walk from the phone company. He was on vacation at the family cottage in Phillips, and his folks were home alone. They were still up when a knock sounded at the front door. Bob Sr. snapped on the porch light, opened the door, and was confronted with a man holding a rifle.

The gunman tried to force his way inside.

"I want Bob!" he yelled. "I want to kill him!"

The elderly man mustered all his strength and somehow managed to close and lock the door, keeping the intruder outside.

"Call for help!" he yelled to his wife. "There's a man outside with a gun!"

She cranked her phone, and the McKeen's drop fell at the switchboard.

"Help us!" she yelled over the receiver while her husband watched the door.

"I think I know who it is," Elden told her. "Lock all your doors and windows and shut your lights off. Stay out of sight, and maybe he'll go away. I'll call for help."

The McKeens followed his instructions. As they sat in the center of their darkened living room, they could see the gunman silhouetted in the glow of the street light outside. Then suddenly he faded away into the night, leaving the couple clinging together in terror.

As soon as Mrs. McKeen hung up, Elden called the town constable. "We've got a guy loose on Rumford Avenue with a gun. He just tried to break into the McKeens."

"I'd better get some back-up," the constable said. "I'll pick up my deputy, and we'll be right up."

Elden warned his neighbors.

Les Bryant, who lived next to the Hathaways, had already gone to bed. The pounding on his door woke him up. He could see the outline of a man with a rifle. Les grabbed his shotgun and silently waited inside, not acknowledging the intruder's knock. He was ready to defend himself.

Elden could hear the commotion next door. He secured all his own doors and windows, shut the lights off, and waited in darkness with a rifle in his hand.

"What's going on?" Barbara called from the bedroom. She had been awakened by the racket next door.

"Just stay put and don't move," Elden commanded. He quietly told her the events of the evening.

"Oh no!" Barbara exclaimed. "He's going to be here next!" She frantically looked about for a weapon to defend herself. She grabbed the first thing she found - a metal section of her vacuum cleaner hose!

"I think I hear someone at the back door," she whispered. For a moment they felt paralyzed with fear. They could hear the door knob being turned as the gunman looked for a way in.

"I know him well enough to talk to him," Elden said.

"Don't you dare!" Barbara demanded. She kept a tight grip on her husband and the vacuum cleaner hose.

They could hear him as he silently circled the house, testing each door and window to see if one had been left unlocked. They watched his shadow pass by the bedroom window. Elden tightly gripped his rifle, hoping it would not be necessary to use it.

"What's keeping the constables?" he wondered. "They should be here by now."

The sounds from outside stopped. Was he gone, or was he waiting? The minutes seemed like hours. Elden returned to the switchboard. A call came in. It was from Sterling Mills across the street.

"He was just here," he told Elden.

"I'd better call the young woman who is renting Stowell's house. I know her husband is at a meeting, and she is home alone with the kids," Elden said.

Elden gave her the warning. "What am I going to do!" She began to panic.

"Shut off your lights. Lock your doors and windows, and hide yourself in the attic with the kids. I'll call you when it's safe to come out."

They reached the attic just in time. They could hear the gunman pounding at their door. They huddled together in fear for their lives. Would he find a way in? Hearts pounding, they waited and waited.

After the gunman left the Stowell's house, he went down the hill to Jim Farrar's. Jim opened the door and confronted him.

"No one will listen to me," the young man pleaded. "They wouldn't call Washington, and I've tried almost every house on the street looking for help, and no-one will open their doors."

"Well now, you don't really want that gun," Jim said. "It probably scared them all." Jim reached out and took the rifle. He placed a call to Elden while the intruder waited peaceably on the porch.

Shortly afterwards the constable and his back-up arrived and took the young man into protective custody. The night of terror on Rumford Avenue was over. It was not until the next day that the neighbors found out that the gun, a 22, was not loaded in the first place.

- - - - - - - - - -

A similar incident occurred a few weeks later. This time Elden was at camp, Barbara was at home, and Tom Thurston was tending the switchboard. It so happened that two psychiatrist friends were visiting Tom at the telephone office. One was the disturbed man's doctor.

As before, the caller wanted the Pentagon, and he was not able to get through.

"I've got a machete, and I've had it with you telephone operators! You're going to pay for not placing my calls!"

He headed up the street again. This time he came straight to the telephone office.

"Don't answer the door!" one of the doctors ordered as the pounding began.

"It's all right," Tom said. "I don't think he'll harm anyone."

The other doctor grabbed one of Elden's rifles and stood behind the door ready to hit the young man over the head at the first sign of violence.

Tom opened the door and greeted him. "Why don't you give me the knife," Tom asked, "and let's talk about your problems."

Thankfully he agreed and was finally able to get the help he needed. When Elden came home the next morning, the machete was still lying next to the switchboard.

Chapter 40

GOOD OLD MAINE HOSPITALITY

"Dear, why don't we have a midwinter party?" Barbara asked her husband. "We need something to break up the doldrums."

"OK with me," Elden agreed.

The family was always involved in something sociable, whether a family gathering, Eastern Star function, or entertaining the visitors who came to see the old crank phone company.

"We'll invite our friends and also have Susan and Linda ask who they want," she said.

The date was set for a couple of weeks away on a Saturday night. The guest list was completed and invitations sent. Barbara planned the menu, baked and froze for several days beforehand. Susan and Linda purchased the decorations and worked out the beverage selections. It was Susan's turn to tend the switchboard the night of the party.

The evening arrived, and the house filled with guests and merriment. Susan dutifully stayed at her post.

"Let me get you another drink, Sue," Sterling Mills offered. "What do you want?"

"A whisky and ginger will do," she said. Soon he was back with a full refill.

"Oh shoot!" she yelled. She had accidentally knocked her drink over, spilling it into the switchboard. "Oh no!" she panicked. "Everything's gone dead! Get me Dad quick!"

A drop came down and she tried to answer it.

"It's no good. I can't hear them."

Elden arrived from the living room. "The drink has shorted out the switchboard," he said. "The only thing we can do is dry it out as soon as possible."

"Barbara," he hollered. "Can you get me all your hair dryers?"

Barbara raced through the house gathering hers and the girls' while Irene Mills ran home across the street for hers. Before long the corner of the living room housing the board was filled with hair dryers and lots of towels.

"OK, I think we've got it," Elden said several minutes later. "Everything seems to be working again. Now no more drinks near the switchboard tonight!"

- - - - - - - - - -

Barbara loved to cook, and her bread and rolls were well known throughout the town. Almost every visitor, including members of the press and TV crews, who came to see the company were well fed.

One antique phone buff from a southern state flew into Boston and hired a limousine to drive him to Bryant Pond. He arrived at the office door wearing his own telephone head set, ready to answer calls. He was really enjoying himself when Barbara noticed that the chauffeur hadn't left the car.

She went outside.

"Won't you come in," she asked.

"No, M'am, I can't do that."

"Why not?"

"Cause I'm supposed to stay out here with the car."

"Not at my house! Now come in and have something to eat," she insisted.

She showed him into the dining room and fed him a meal. He was not used to being treated in this manner, but after a while he was able to relax, and their conversation turned to his limosine driving.

"Would you like to go for a ride?" he asked her.

"You're kidding! I've never been in a car like that. Maybe just a short one," she said with a twinge of excitement.

He took her down through the village.

"Boy!" she said. "I can just hear all the townsfolk talking about this!"

The chauffeur enjoyed himself so much at the Hathaways that he told Barbara, "Anytime you want to come to Boston, you will have the use of a limo for the day free."

However, she was always too busy to take him up on his offer.

- - - - - - - - - -

One miserable November evening, Elden answered a knock at the door. The ground outside was covered with a thin wet layer of ice from a freezing rain.

"Can I make a phone call here?" asked the man standing on the steps.

"You sure can," Elden replied. "Come in."

"When I left Massachusetts, the weather was fine. I'm heading for Andover to join some friends deer hunting, but I've got summer tires on the car, and the roads are just too slippery to drive."

He convinced one of his friends with a four-wheel-drive to come from Andover after him.

"Do you mind if I wait here?" he asked.

Barbara was in the process of fixing grilled cheese sandwiches for supper and asked the traveler to join them. He reluctantly agreed, not wanting to inconvenience his hosts.

Eventually his friends arrived, and he passed Elden a ten dollar bill as he prepared to leave.

"Does this cover what I owe you?" he asked.

"The only thing you owe me is 25 cents for the phone calls," Elden replied, handing him back the money.

"Yes, but you fed me and let me wait in here where it's warm."

"Well, it's a bad night, and besides, it's nice having company," Elden smiled.

The man paid for his call, thanked Barbara and Elden and continued on to Andover. A month later the Hathaways received a large package in the mail filled with S.S. Pierce goodies. The card read, "Thanks for helping the traveler in the storm."

Chapter 40 - GOOD OLD MAINE HOSPITALITY
Photograph by Hathaway

"One antique phone buff from a southern state flew into Boston and hired a limousine to drive him to Bryant Pond."

Chapter 41

MAKING IT FOR TWENTY-FIVE YEARS

As it is in many small New England towns, the citizens of Bryant Pond have always been a close knit community. Social functions center around the churches, the Masonic orders and the Grange. The people celebrate together and grieve together. Neighbors bring food to families as a way of sharing their love and concern. When a tragedy occurs, such as an accident or a fire, someone always spearheads a collection of food, clothes, money, or whatever is needed. The telephone company usually acted as the information center, giving out the news and directing calls to helping hands.

For the Hathaways, community involvement had been a way of life, even before the switchboard came into their house. They laughed, mourned, and celebrated with their extended family of telephone customers. Twenty-five years had passed unbelievably fast.

"Mom and Dad have given so much to the town, I think we should have a big party for the twenty-fifth anniversary of their purchase of the telephone company," Susan suggested, consulting with the employees. "After Labor Day when business has quieted down would be a perfect time."

She spent a lot of time planning the occasion. Bob McKeen made the invitations for the meal which were sent to 100 of the Hathaways' relatives and friends. "Let's see - we'll have to hire the Legion Hall in Locke Mills, get the Birthday Club to cook and serve the meal, Leona Flint to make a special cake...maybe we can get Mike's band to come from New Hampshire to play for dancing. All of our subscribers will be invited to join the fun after the dinner is finished. There just wouldn't be enough room for everyone to eat!"

Bob also made the table favors. The employees chipped in to buy flowers for the head table and corsages for the honored guests.

The date was September 11, 1976. The evening was a huge success. Barbara and Elden were given a well deserved tribute for their twenty-five years of service. Over two hundred people crowded into the Legion Hall for the after-dinner festivities, dancing the night away.

It was one of the best parties the town had had since its 150 year birthday party some ten years before. Needless to say, before the evening was over, Elden found his way to the drums to play a few tunes.

Chapter 42

ELDEN ALWAYS WANTED A CABOOSE

One evening at a wedding reception where Elden was playing drums with the dance band, a railroad friend came over to visit.

"Say, how much will you give me for my caboose?" he asked, half-joking.

"What do you mean?" Elden asked.

"I bought one of those old ones the railroad had for sale, and now I find I can't afford to move it, so I guess I'm going to have to get rid of it."

"How much do you want?" Elden asked, now very interested.

His friend told him the price.

"I'll take it!" he said without a moment's hesitation. He had always wanted to have his own caboose, ever since he was a kid.

"You bought a WHAT?" Barbara said the next morning as he explained his purchase to her. "WHERE are we going to put a caboose!"

"We've got just enough room at the edge of the woods right next to the lawn. I'll have Sterl Mills truck in some gravel and level it off for the ties and rail." He had it all figured out before he told his wife.

"How are you going to figure out how to put it together?" Barbara asked.

"Well, I've been working on the railroad for forty years - I guess I should be able to do it."

"What do you say, boys," he asked the section crew. "If I get a case of beer, will you come up some night and help me lay track?"

They were more than willing to help. He purchased some second-hand rails and ties, and eight men made short work of preparing Elden's railroad bed. Elden made the grade slope slightly towards the road so the caboose wouldn't roll the other way, down the bank and into the bog.

He paid the Canadian National Railroad $110 to have it delivered over the tracks from Portland to Bryant Pond. Stowell's Mill gave permission to leave it on their siding for a few days before it could be moved to its new resting place. A contractor with a large flatbed and crane was hired to hoist it onto the truck and haul it through town and up Rumford Avenue.

The easiest way to move it was to jack the caboose up and bring half the wheels over on the first trip. This took all morning, and after lunch the crew removed the second set and dropped the body of the caboose down onto the low bed of the truck. A couple of linemen rode on the roof to lift the telephone wires over the structure since it exceeded the road's legal height limits.

They started off slowly without anyone to direct traffic. However, they soon encountered the local constable.

"Do you want some help?" he asked.

"That would be great," Elden replied.

The officer hurried home for his hat and badge, and helped direct them around the sharp corner in the center of town. He was aided by some Canadian travelers on their way to Old Orchard, who controlled the traffic coming from the north. More volunteers came to their aid, stopping cars as the procession made the turn onto Rumford Avenue. Finally they arrived at the telephone company office, and the newly laid rail bed.

The job of reassembling the caboose and the wheels proved to be a tedious task. It took the crane several hours to maneuver the wooden structure into the right position. While this was going on, deputy sheriff Barney Bartlett drove by.

"You want me to direct traffic for you?" he asked Elden.

"Yeh, Barney, that would be great," he replied.

"You do have all the proper permits, don't you?" the deputy wanted to know.

"Sure do - the mover took care of all that."

Barney proceeded to hold up vehicles traveling the avenue, and by late in the afternoon, the caboose was firmly in place. Elden thanked Barney for his help, and after the deputy left, he asked the mover, "You did get the permits to move that thing on the state highway, didn't you?"

"No," he replied, I thought you were going to!"

They looked at each other, and Elden just laughed in relief. "I guess we were fortunate we didn't get caught."

At last the caboose had found a new home, and the Hathaways made plans to have it all spruced up for the county's bicentennial celebration. Barbara cleaned and washed the insides while the telephone crew gave its outsides a new coat of paint. Festive bunting was hung from the windows and end rail as the 4th of July approached. It didn't take long for the caboose to become more popular with visiting children than the switchboard. They couldn't wait for a chance to sit up in the lookout seat, the place high up in the middle section of the caboose where railroad men watched out for the safety of the train.

Chapter 42 - ELDEN ALWAYS WANTED A CABOOSE
Photograph by UPI, 1981

The caboose even served as a temporary home for one of the linemen who'd had a spat with his wife.

Chapter 43

THE NIGERIAN CONNECTION

This is a true story of an early scam attempt. Names have been changed to protect any living relatives.

- - - - - - - - -

Jim True enjoyed reading the London Times, one of his few links with the outside world. The climate and accommodations of interior Nigeria, where he was currently employed by the government, provided few comforts. As a supervisor in charge of constructing a new road, he often found himself as an intermediary between the various factions vying for control of the African nation. He had learned to play in the shadowy world of white contraband in Vietnam. He had made a small fortune on the black market, acquiring and selling American goods for large profits.

In the Times he read with great interest the account of the Bryant Pond, Maine residents' plea to the Public Utilities Commission to keep their small telephone company hand crank.

He dashed off a cable. "Dear sirs, Hoorah for the Bryant Pond Telephone Company. Down with all Commissions. Do you need dollars?" signed, Jim True, Nigeria.

Barbara and Elden were amazed that the story had reached so far around the world. They politely sent back a reply thanking Jim, "but we do not need any money at this time".

True and the Hathaways continued to correspond over the next few years, becoming friends by mail. Jim kept them appraised of his health, often writing from a hospital bed. He suffered from asthma.

Eventually his health improved enough for him to plan a visit to the United States. He wanted to come to Bryant Pond to see the Hathaways and the company. He and his Asian wife flew into Portland where Barbara and Elden met them at the airport.

Although Barbara issued an invitation to stay at their house, Jim insisted on staying at a motel. The closest one was in South Paris, about 20 miles away.

They had an enjoyable visit with the Hathaways their first day. Barbara and Elden showed them the beautiful western Maine countryside, and they spent time with the old crank phone company. All the employees had become involved in the Trues' story and looked forward to meeting them.

One of Jim's first stops in Maine was the state liquor store. He purchased a large supply, being careful to include the Hathaways' favorite brands. That evening as the men drank and talked together, Jim revealed a major concern.

"You know," he said, "I make a great deal of money from the Nigerian government. The problem is, it doesn't do me any good outside of their country. I can't take it with me. I have to spend it there."

"Do you plan to continue to live there?" Elden asked.

"Oh no," Jim replied. "We want to come back to the United States to retire, but I need the Nigerian funds in order to do it."

"What are you going to do?" asked Elden.

"I need to come up with a way to get my money out of the country. I've given it a great deal of thought. I use American heavy construction equipment to build the road," he continued. "If I had someone in this country to purchase the equipment, they could ship it to Nigeria with an inflated bill of sale. That way, when I pay the bill, the difference can be deposited in a U.S. bank account. Within a year or so, I'll be able to get my money out of the country, and we can come back to America to retire."

Elden didn't know what to say.

"I was thinking," Jim said slowly and sincerely, "you might be the one to head up the company that ships the goods from this country. The hour is getting late, and I'm tired. We can discuss this matter tomorrow," he concluded. The men joined the women, and the Hathaways drove them back to their motel.

The next day Jim developed some trouble breathing. The change in climate was aggravating his asthma problem.

"We wish you'd stay here tonight where we can keep an eye on you," Barbara worried.

"No, we don't want to put you out."

"You wouldn't be any trouble," Barbara urged.

Despite her pleas, the Trues insisted on returning to their room in South Paris.

"If you have any problems, call, and I'll be right down," Elden told them as he left for home.

It was still early when Mrs. True called to say that her husband was having a serious asthma attack.

Barbara called the South Paris rescue squad, and Elden rushed back to their motel room. By the time he arrived, Jim was feeling better, responding fairly rapidly to a shot of his medicine.

I think he will be all right now," Mrs. True said. She thanked Elden and the rescue members for coming so promptly.

At 3 a.m. she called the Hathaways again. "He's much worse. I have never seen him this way. I don't know what to do!"

"I'll be right there," said Elden, reaching for his clothes. "In the meantime, we'll call the rescue squad again."

"We'd better get him to emergency right off," the ambulance crew told her when they arrived. "His condition is serious."

Elden and Mrs. True followed the ambulance to the hospital. They waited and waited in the emergency room lounge. Finally the doctor approached. "I'm afraid we couldn't save him," he said sadly. "His heart was just too weak."

The shock of the news sent Mrs. True into an ancient Asian death wail, something Mainers hadn't seen before. There was nothing they could do to comfort her.

The Hathaways spent the next day locating the dead man's relatives scattered throughout the country. Many had unlisted numbers, but Elden convinced the local operators in their calling area to put "death notification" calls through.

Arrangements to ship the body were made. Susan helped take care of the airline travel arrangements for both the casket and the widow who had never traveled alone. Eventually she returned to her homeland and continued to correspond with Barbara.

Would Elden have become involved in Jim True's scam? Probably not, but it would have been tempting.

Chapter 44

RAISING THE RATES WASN'T ENOUGH

The 1970's saw a rapid growth in the Bryant Pond hand crank phone company. Despite the local support of the hearing of '73 and their growing notoriety throughout the country, Barbara and Elden saw their company making less and less profit. They did not pay themselves a salary. Elden's railroad retirement was the basis of their support. As the company was a utility, they could not capitalize on tourist dollars as some other businesses were able to do.

"We've had to add so much help and equipment that our

expenses are more than the income generated by new subscribers, monthly service fees and toll calls. We are going to have to get a rate increase!" Elden concluded to his wife.

They petitioned the P.U.C. and were granted a 47% hike in May of 1977. Residential phone rates went from $3 to $4.90, and business rates from $4 to $5.90. By this time over 60% of the customers had their own private lines. Others were on a list waiting for more cable to be run. The increase amounted to $7000 a year which would help ease the pressure for the moment, but a complicated settlement agreement between New England Telephone and independent telephone companies in disbursement of toll call revenue cut down on the amount of monetary return for the Bryant Pond Telephone Company.

"We used to get a check each month, and now we have to send them over $1000," Elden complained to his children. "You add this to our labor cost, and Mother and I can't afford to draw a salary." They were going in the hole financially.

The volume of calls increased to the point that two operators had all they could do to handle peak hour traffic. Billing and bookkeeping were now full time jobs. The Hathaways felt as if the company was splitting apart at the seams. These problems were not evident to the townspeople, to the many visitors who flocked to town to see the system, or the media who wrote of a community trying to hold onto a vanishing way of life. The pressure on the couple continued to build. They didn't have the energy to keep up the frantic pace any more. Something would have to give.

"Your mother and I are looking seriously at selling the company," Elden told Mike at a 1979 August outing on top of Mount Washington. "We just can't handle it anymore. The Utility Commission rules are all geared for the larger companies. You know, one customer could ruin us. Someone could run up a toll bill of over a thousand dollars. If I cut off their service, by law I'd have to hook them up again if another member of the family requested it. I lost over $2000 last year in bad debts. We're literally being forced out of business. We just want to retire and spend some time at camp. Our main concern is that we do what is best for the customers who have supported us all these years."

Mike talked to his sisters Susan and Linda, and they decided to study the feasibility of purchasing the company from their parents.

"We really think you're crazy to consider it," the couple warned. "It'll take a lot of money to change to dial, and the Utility Commission is not interested in the historical nostalgia of the old hand crank phones. They're concerned about the service."

Barbara and Elden were right. It was not feasible for the children to continue in the old way. They started looking for new owners from outside the family.

Chapter 45

REAL PEOPLE AND THE LAST HAND CRANK

As the Hathaways put out the word of their desire to sell, the American love affair with the telephone company continued.

Real People wanted to do a feature on the company.

Word spread through the operators like wildfire. It was the most popular TV show in America. Skip Stephenson and his crew flew into Boston in the midst of the October foliage season. After staying overnight at the Bethel Inn, they started out bright and early the next morning to capture the local countryside with their cameras.

The star of the show watched the operators as they answered the calls, then asked if he could take a turn at the switchboard. It didn't take him long to completely bungle up the service. Some of the customers were not too understanding.

"What the hell's going on!" Elden's voice boomed from a phone in the basement.

The camera crew chuckled in the background as they recorded

his words which would eventually be aired.

Barbara, always the perfect hostess, prepared a New England boiled dinner for everyone, but time was so tight that the crew had to gulp their meal down between takes. By the middle of the afternoon, the Real People production company was on its way to the next story in upstate New York.

Before their departure, Skip was presented with a hand carved wood plaque designed by Penny Hathaway and made by Mike. It read, "Crank Calls in Bryant Pond, Maine Are Made By Real People". Perhaps a part of the memory of the Bryant Pond Telephone Company may still hang in some producer's Los Angeles office.

- - - - - - - - - - -

Grand River, Iowa, the only other magneto system left in the country, decided to change to dial by a 121-73 vote of its customers in March of 1979. Nine months later, and at a cost of $800,000 they completed the cutover. On December 6, 1979, Ruth Bowles, 77, who along with her husband had managed the Grand River company for 39 years before they retired in 1977, called Bryant Pond, Maine.

"This is our last call on the crank phones, and you are now the last one left in the country. We wish you the best." The Hathaways were now the only working link to the telephone's historic past.

"Well, we've done it," Elden said to Barbara later that evening as the board quieted down. In the middle of their amazing accomplishment, they felt a strange sort of loneliness. They were the last survivor of a vanishing way of life.

An article appearing in a Philadelphia paper summed it up: "There remains just one hope, and that lies in tiny Bryant Pond, Maine, which may be the only place left in America that still can provide a human voice at the other end of the line. It is a thin thread by which civilization dangles."

Chapter 45 - REAL PEOPLE AND THE LAST HAND CRANK
Photograph by Bill Haynes, Portland Press Herald, 1980

"Real People wanted to do a feature on the company." Pictured in doorway are Elden (L) and Skip Stephenson (R).

Chapter 45 - REAL PEOPLE AND THE LAST HAND CRANK
Photograph by Bill Haynes, Portland Press Herald, 1980

"The star of the show watched the operators as they answered the calls."

Chapter 45 - REAL PEOPLE AND THE LAST HAND CRANK
Photograph by Bill Haynes, Portland Press Herald, 1980

"Skip was presented with a hand carved wood plaque..." Pictured L to R: Susan, Barbara, Skip, Elden, Linda.

Chapter 46

DOES ANYONE WANT TO BUY A TELEPHONE COMPANY?

By 1980, the cost of operating the old crank phone company had soared to almost $100,000 per year. The Hathaways were convinced more than ever that it was time to sell. Elden discussed strategies with his wife.

"I'm going to contact Delta Electronics and the Continental Phone Company. They have been buying up a lot of Maine independents. I think I'll also give Clarence Todd a call at the Oxford County Telephone & Telegraph Company and see if they might be interested."

Delta quickly responded, sending a representative to evaluate the company, and a few weeks later, they made an offer.

After studying the proposal, Elden told Barbara, "I can't see going this way. It's primarily an offer to give us stock in their company. That won't provide any retirement income."

Continental never responded to the query.

Finding a buyer was a slow process.

Yankee Magazine ran an article in its February 1981 issue entitled "Ever Wish You Owned the Phone Company?" It brought a little interest but no concrete offers. Headlines throughout America varied from "Crank Phone Still Going Strong in Maine Town" to "Crank Phones Fading".

In the spring, negotiations started in earnest with Oxford County Tel & Tel. Elden had several meetings with Clarence Todd and Oxford general manager Bob Jamison.

"Whatever you do, try to hold onto the old phones," Mike requested of his father. "There will be a big demand to buy them after the cutover, and they could be a very important part of your

Chapter 46 - DOES ANYONE WANT TO BUY A TELEPHONE COMPANY?
Photograph by Bill Haynes, 1981

"On July 23rd, 1981 (they) traveled to the Oxford County Telephone Company headquarters in Buckfield." Pictured L to R: Elden, Barbara, Clarence Todd, Bob Jamison.

Chapter 46 - DOES ANYONE WANT TO BUY A TELEPHONE COMPANY?
Photograph by Bill Haynes, 1981

"Bill Haynes quoted Elden... 'It hurt to see it go, but there was no way I could keep it...'"

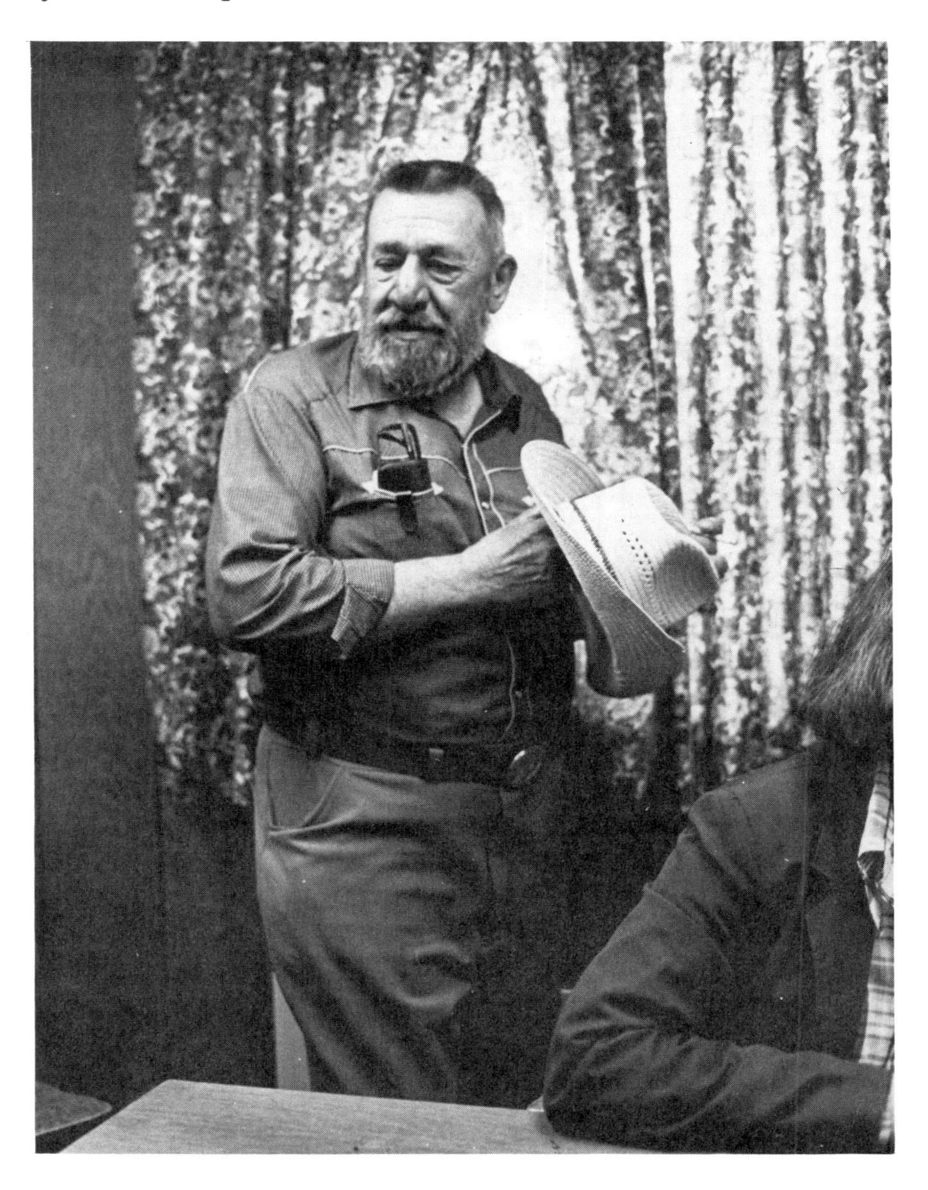

retirement."

Oxford did not want the phones but did not want the public to become part of the sale. It was agreed to have the lawyers representing both sides draw up and sign an agreement giving the Hathaways ownership of the phones.

All the details were worked out, and the purchase plan was presented to the Public Utilities Commission for approval. The OK came July 3, 1981. On July 23rd, Barbara, Elden, Susan, Linda, Bob McKeen and their lawyer Mary Ann Smith, traveled to the Oxford County Telephone Company headquarters in Buckfield. They were joined by Bob Jamison, Clarence Todd and their accountant and lawyer.

Reporter Bill Haynes quoted Elden in the next day's Portland Press Herald, "I'm sad but I'm glad at the same time. It hurt to see it go, but there was no way I could keep the thing going and pay for it out of my own pocket. I hope we've made the right decision for the community."

Chapter 47

DON'T YANK THE CRANK

The day after the P.U.C. decision the newspaper headlines read "Hand Cranked Phones Yielding to Touch Tones".

Bryant Pond went into shock. They knew the company was for sale, but the reality did not set in until the purchase was finalized. Bryant Pond would soon become just another small town.

Within a few days, a couple of young men who had recently moved to the community decided to organize a movement to halt the changeover to dial. "Don't Yank the Crank" became the theme of their campaign. By the end of the first week of August they had already collected over 500 signatures on a petition calling for the continuation of the magneto service.

An open meeting to all interested citizens was held September 1 at the Town Hall. It was standing room only. "Don't Yank the Crank" T-shirts were sold to help with the fundraising. By meeting time over a thousand signatures of support had been collected. A lawyer specializing in utilities was hired. He advised the group on submitting a complaint to the Public Utilities Commission. That complaint was received in Augusta September 25, 1981.

The media spotlight continued to shine on the town. "Good Morning America" came in October. Early in December the chief lawyer for the P.U.C. recommended the complaint against the new owners be heard. In the meantime Oxford had gone ahead with plans to upgrade the outside lines and purchased land on Rumford Avenue a half mile beyond the Hathaways to house the new dial equipment.

The date for the hearing was set for February 11, 1982. The location was Bryant Pond's gymnasium. There would be two sessions, one from 1:30-4:50 p.m. and the other from 6:30 p.m. on into the evening. Larry Billings submitted a poem to the February 4th Bethel Citizen that represented the thoughts of more than 70% of the Bryant Pond residents:

"Bryant Pond Phone Company
writer wrote a tribute
to the talking dead.
But here the slender lines
convey the life of all the town,
and visitors in droves descend
to add to the renown
of a breathing, vibrant thing,
sprung from out of the past,
and a nation stops to grasp
the value and the worth of this,
the best, the lone, the last."

The hearing was jammed, and it went well into the night with 170 still in attendance after a 10 p.m. recess. The debate over change went on. Those for change questioned the invasion of privacy by the old system and inferior service in comparison to the modern dial equipment. Those opposed to change pleaded for nostalgia and the right for the customers to decide which service they wanted. The P.U.C. collected its information and adjourned to weigh the decision.

Time and People magazines came to Maine to report on the conflict. The battle waged on into the first half of 1982.

Chapter 48

CAN I BUY AN OLD PHONE?

Requests to purchase old crank phones had started trickling in during the late 1970's. Once the stories of a pending sale broke, the demand turned into a flood. At first Barbara graciously answered each letter, but the amount of requests and letters of support became overwhelming.

Dear Hathaway Family,

I don't know if you remember me -- I lived in Bryant Pond for a year during 1970-71 -- and loved it. I''m very sad to see the end of the crank phone system. I know you invested a lot of your lives in the company--you were the company. I still remember one night when we couldn't get up the hill to our place & you took us in & gave us dinner til the snowplows came. A lot of changes have happened to all of us...and now this dramatic change to Bryant Pond. Well, life must go on, but I want you to know how much I appreciated you.

(from Sacramento, CA)

Dear Mr. Mayor,

I read in our local paper that your town has converted from crank telephones. I hate to see the end of an era but I guess thats the price of progress. I remember the dialless phones with the separate wooden crank operated box...I remember my father bringing home such a set and my childish way of destroying it...My point is, now that I'm mature and have a home of my own, I'm trying to recapture the past.

The article I read said the residents were being allowed to purchase their sets...perhaps you know a town resident who would like to sell me their set at a fair price...

(from Valatie, NY)

Dear Sir,

I saw you on the "Today" show today.

It must be a pleasure to live in such a lovely little town.. The people looked as if they were the salt of the earth. I saw the old crank type telephones on TV. Do you have any extra ones you will sell?...

I would love to hear from you, and I think the old song, "I Love Those Dear Hearts and Gentle People" that live in my home town applies to your town - and my town...

(from Archer City, TX)

Mr. Hathaway,

I thought you might like a copy of your article from the Oregonian for your scrapbook. I don't know why but it brought tears to my eyes. I guess it's an end of an era. Thanks.

(from Oregon)

Dear Mr. Hathaway,

I guess I sound simple, but I have nostalgia so bad for the old way that it sort of gives me a longing feeling. I was sad to hear your town is changing its phones. There isn't much left of our history and old times. Do you think I could have a chance of buying one of the old cabinet wall crank phones? Also one of the candlestick phones? I saw them years ago for sale but could not afford them. I am now 62 and totally disabled. It's now or never.

(from Secaucus, NJ)

Dear Mrs. Hathaway,

My family & I thought we would let you know how sad we are to read today that the Bryant Pond hand-cranked telephone system is finally closing. The news was in the national daily paper ...and it came as a great surprise to us. We had the pleasure & privilege of visiting your unique exchange last year whilst on holiday in New England, and it was great to see a living piece of American history still in action. We are sure the telephone company replacing the exchange are making a sad mistake in this respect.

Lets hope that it can be preserved in a museum somewhere, because of course the history of communication is as important as the history of transport or military vehicles etc. etc.

Anyway we thought you might take a bit of comfort knowing that not only do you have 529 unhappy subscribers, but 530, the ------ family.

(from England)

It was July 2nd when the P.U.C. handed down its opinion. Oxford could change to dial. Plans started to make the old phones available to collectors. The papers carried a UPI story called "What Ma Bell Calls Trash, Maine May Call Cash". After reading the article, the lawyers for the "Don't Yank the Crank Committee" thought they had found a loophole in the purchase agreement between Oxford Tel and the Hathaways. The group hastily decided to petition the P.U.C. to reopen the case. They questioned who actually owned the old phones. Other citizens of town organized a counter-movement collecting signatures to allow Barbara and Elden to keep the phones. They presented the secretary of the Commission a petition with 342 names on it. Two days later it was decided to postpone the appeal until both sides could be heard. The conversion to dial remained stalled until the rehearing. In the meantime the crank company and the Hathaways continued on.

"Elden has a call from the Johnny Carson Show!" The excited operator tracked him down.

"We've been following the story of the Bryant Pond crank phone company, and we'd be interested in having you come to Los Angeles and be on the 'Tonight Show'," the representative explained. "Would you like to come out?"

"Yes, I'm definitely interested," Elden replied, "but I don't go any place without my wife."

"Normally we fly our guests first class, but we could arrange for two tourist tickets for you and your wife if that's acceptable." he said.

"Two tourist seats will be fine," Elden assured him.

The trip was set for two weeks before the final hearing on September 22.

At the hearing, the primary focal point was the value and disposition of the old phones. Oxford testified that they did not want them. A P.U.C. engineer stated that they were virtually worthless. Elden was unable to show which phones were his personal property and which had belonged to the company. The Commission gathered the testimony and left to weigh the arguments.

The end of October brought the final word from the P.U.C. They decreed that the telephones belonged to the Bryant Pond Telephone Company and were considered part of the inventory sold to the Oxford Telephone & Telegraph Company. Elden and Barbara had lost. It was decided by the Commission and the new owners to sell the magnetos that were in service to the customers for three dollars each. Finally, in February 1986, Elden was able to purchase the remaining inventory of phones that had been stored in his garage after the sale.

Chapter 48 - CAN I BUY AN OLD PHONE?
Photograph by Jack Quinn, Lewiston Daily Sun, 1973

"Finally...Elden was able to purchase the remaining inventory...stored in his garage after the sale." Pictured L to R: Bob McKeen, Elden.

Chapter 49

THE CUTOVER

Finally the way was cleared for Oxford County Tel & Tel to complete its plan to change Bryant Pond to dial. There was a lot to be accomplished. New phone equipment had to be purchased and a building built to house it. Cable needed to be strung and the dial phones installed. While the work progressed, the telephone switchboards remained at the Hathaways. The only difference was that Barbara and Elden didn't have to worry about running it anymore. All the operators, including Susan and Linda, now worked for Oxford County Tel and Tel.

The date for the cutover was set for October 11, 1983 at 2:00 p.m. The new push button phones were installed side by side with the old crank phones. Invitations were sent out for the final ceremony. Representing the family, Susan and Linda tended the switchboards during the final minutes. Bob Jamison placed the last call to one of Oxford's employees who was recovering from surgery in a Portland hospital. The office was filled to the collapsing point with TV cameras and photographers everywhere. At 2:12 p.m. the carbons were pulled from the main-frame in a corner of the office.

The last old hand crank system was no more.

- - - - - - - - - -

As the crowd filed out of the room to attend a cutover party at the Legion Hall in Locke Mills, a strange silence descended over the Hathaway home. For the first time in more than thirty years, the switchboards stood lifeless. It was as if a member of the family had just passed away. And so it had.

- - - - - - - - - -

Even years later when family reunions got a little noisy, you might hear someone say, "Keep it down so the operators can hear! Who's supposed to be tending the board, anyway?"

Chapter 49 - THE CUTOVER
Photograph by Bill Haynes, 1983

"Representing the family, Susan (L) and Linda (R) tended the switchboard during the final moments." Elden and Barbara looked on.

"GOODBYE OPERATOR"

Composed and Sung by Linda Hathaway Stowell for Cutover Day, October 11, 1983

In Bryant Pond there lived a family
And Hathaway was their name.
In their living room was a switchboard
That led them down the path to fame.

> Operator, Operator,
> won't you ring that girl of mine?
> I've been trying now for hours,
> But she's on a party line.

Elden & Barbara were the owners
And their children numbered three.
They were Michael, Susan, Linda,
And they all worked there for free.

> Elden worked days on the railroad,
> Then at nite he'd climb the poles.
> So - Barbara manned the switchboard
> And baked the best darn bread & rolls.

They never realized when they bought it
That it could grow more than they planned,
So they bought a second switchboard
And hired some folks to lend a hand.

> There were many operators
> Pushing plugs there all day long.
> Over 30 years they've worked there.
> This is why I sing this song.

Night & day, winter, summer
Through every kind of weather,
They became a little family
As they worked so close together.

Many years passed & the town grew
And the time for change was due.
From a crank phone to a dial phone
This would all be something new.

So they sold their little company
To Oxford County Tel & Tel.
This would be the first vacation
For the Old Crank & Ma Bell.

Operator, Operator,
Thanks for trying all this while.
But I guess I'll hang the crank up,
Say "Farewell" to you and use my dial.

OPERATORS

Bean, Susan Ellsworth
Bennett, Luna Farrington
Berryment, Genneth
Berryment, Tony
Billings, Barbara Berryment
Billings, Tamara Mills
Buck, Margaret
Davis, Carol
Davis, Norma
Farnum, Ester
Farnum, Evelyn
Farnum, Frances
Farrington, Debbie
Fraser, Linda
Glines, Susan Hathaway
Hathaway, Althea
Hathaway, Barbara
Hathaway, Elden
Hathaway, Michael
Hinckley, Andrew
Hoyt, Andrea
Judkins, Howard
Judkins, Sylvia
Keen, Elinor Andrews
Keen, Jim
Kuvaja, Beryle
Mason, Evelyn Bean
McAllister, Lelia
McKeen, Robert Jr.
McLean, Marguerite
Meserve, Herbert
Meserve, Viola
Mills, Rachel
Olson, Debra Morgan
Poland, Virginia Morgan
Redmond, Karia Hobbs
Stowell, Linda Hathaway
Swan, Denise Noyes
Taylor, Kathy
Thurston, Tom
Webber, Jeff
Wheeler, Margaret
Whitman, Orene

Aube, Bruce
Bennett, Dean
Berry, Richard
Billings, Robert
Cary, Paul
Cary, Rodney
Farnum, Fred
Green, Basil
Hammond, Gerald
Hathaway, Elden
Hathaway, Michael
Hathaway, Rupert "Putt"
Hinckley, Andrew
Johnson, Chuck
Judkins, Howard
Keen, Jim
Koumalainen, Craig
MacKillop, Howard
McAllister, Charlie
McInnis, Stuart
McKeen, Robert Jr.
Meserve, Herbert
Mills, Blaine
Mitchell, Robert
Powers, Hugh
Raymond, Fred
Redman, Tom
Rogers, Richard
Thurston, Tom
Webber, Jeff
Wing, Elmer "Pete"

INDEX OF NAMES CHAPTERS

LI -Linemen; OP - Operator